A STUDENT'S GUIDE TO MATH SUCCESS

Overcoming Barriers

Delbert Ferster, Ann M. Heath, and Mary Elizabeth Jones

cognella® | ACADEMIC PUBLISHING

Bassim Hamadeh, CEO and Publisher
Kassie Graves, Acquisitions Editor
Berenice Quirino, Associate Production Editor
Emely Villavicencio, Senior Graphic Designer
Alexa Lucido, Licensing Associate
Don Kesner, Interior Designer
Natalie Piccotti, Senior Marketing Manager
Kassie Graves, Director of Acquisitions and Sales
Jamie Giganti, Senior Managing Editor

ISBN: 978-1-5165-2458-7 (pbk)

A STUDENT'S GUIDE
TO MATH SUCCESS

DEDICATION

A Student's Guide to Math Success: Overcoming Barriers is dedicated to all students who struggle with math anxiety, and whose willingness to persevere shows that the right mindset can pave the pathway for future success.

THE COGNELLA SERIES ON STUDENT SUCCESS

S tudent success isn't always measured in straight As.

Many students arrive at college believing that if they study hard and earn top grades, their higher education experience will be a success. Few recognize that some of their greatest learning opportunities will take place outside the classroom. Learning how to manage stress, navigate new relationships, or put together a budget can be just as important as acing a pop quiz.

The Cognella Series on Student Success is a collection of books designed to help students develop the essential life and learning skills needed to support a happy, healthy, and productive higher education experience. Featuring topics suggested by students and books written by experts, the series offers research-based, yet practical advice to help any student navigate new challenges and succeed throughout their college experience.

Series Editor: Richard Parsons, Ph.D.
Professor of Counselor Education, West Chester University

Other titles available in the series:

- *A Student's Guide to Stress Management*
- *A Student's Guide to a Meaningful Career*
- *A Student's Guide to Self-Care*
- *A Student's Guide to Money Matters*
- *A Student's Guide to Self-Presentation*
- *A Student's Guide to Exercise for Improving Health*
- *A Student's Guide to College Transition*
- *A Student's Guide to College Success*

ABOUT THE AUTHORS

Does the thought of a college-level mathematics course fill you with anxiety and dread? With a little practical advice and positivity, you can easily and effectively put your math-related fears to rest!

A Students Guide to Math Success: Overcoming Barriers provides you with a toolbox of strategies to help you approach math courses with a positive attitude, overcome the key stressors associated with learning mathematics, and develop skills that will help you study efficiently and succeed in your coursework. With this guide, you'll learn how to conquer anxiety, develop healthy habits, and build a positive, personal awareness about how to study mathematics.

Highly approachable and full of practical advice, this guide will help you develop both the mindset and the skill sets needed to build confidence in your personal mathematical ability.

A Student's Guide to Math Success is part of the Cognella Series on Student Success, a collection of books designed to help students develop the essential life and learning skills needed to support a happy, healthy, and productive higher education experience.

Delbert Ferster is a lecturer in mathematics in the Natural and Computational Sciences Department at Immaculata University and supervisor of the Math Center. He earned his Ed.D. in educational leadership at Immaculata University and his M.S. in educational technology at Philadelphia University.

Ann M. Heath is the director of the Higher Education Program at Immaculata University, where she previously served as an associate professor of mathematics and the vice president for academic affairs. She earned her Ph.D. in mathematics at Bryn Mawr College and her M.A. in mathematics at Villanova University.

Mary Elizabeth Jones is a professor of mathematics and computing in the Natural and Computational Sciences Department at Immaculata University. She earned her Ph.D. in information studies at Drexel University and her M.A. in mathematics at Villanova University.

BRIEF CONTENTS

DETAILED CONTENTS

EDITOR'S PREFACE

T he transition to college marks a significant milestone in a person's life. Many of you will be preparing to live away from your friends and family for the very first time. This is and should be an exciting time. It is a time to experience new things and experiment with new options. While the opportunity to grow is clear—so are the many challenges you are to experience as you transition from high school to college.

Research suggests that the first year of college is the most challenging period of adjustment a student faces. Not only will you be required to adjust to new academic demands but you will also have to navigate some social and emotional challenges that accompany your life as a college student. The books found within this series—*Cognella Series on Student Success*—have been developed to help you with the many issues confronting your successful transition from life as a high school student to life as a collegiate. Each book within the series was designed to provide research-based, yet *practical* advice to assist you succeeding in your college experience.

One area in which many students bring 'baggage' from their previous academic experience is in the field of mathematics. Math can be one of the subjects that you either love or hate and fear. If you tend to fall closer to the hate/fear end of the spectrum, then *A Student's Guide to Math Success* is designed for you.

A Student's Guide to Math Success demystifies and de-terrorizes mathematics. While presenting research-informed concepts, it does so within the context of real-life student stories. The practical tips and useful strategies offered will provide you with the tools to not only approach your college mathematics courses with a new, positive sense of self and a healthy expectation for success but will guide you to the achievement of that academic success.

As with all of the books in this series, the information provided has been drawn from established theory and empirical research. However, it is important to note that this is NOT a textbook (you have enough of those), nor is it intended to be dry and 'academic.' Instead, this book, as is true for all the books in the series, has been written to be a useful guide for the reader. To this end, the authors help you see the practical value of the information shared through their use of case illustrations in a feature called *"Voices From Campus."* In addition to understanding the concepts presented as well as their application by way of the case illustration you will be invited to apply what you learned by way of a feature called *"Your Turn."*

The integration of reliable information within a format that encourages your application makes this book, as well as the other books within the series, a useful guide to your successful transition from high school to college.

Richard Parsons, Ph.D.
Series Editor

AUTHORS' PREFACE

Math is tough for all sorts of people and for many different reasons. If you find math challenging, then taking a math class as you start college can be worrisome and upsetting. You are entering college with a great sense of new beginnings, aspiration, and expectation. With all that is new and hopeful, you also bring with you your academic background, personal sense of identity, and emotional/psychological baggage. You might be facing the requirement to study a course in college mathematics with fear and dread knowing that the past has been a traumatic or, at the very least, unpleasant experience. Mathematics is often a building-block prerequisite for majors, careers, and advancement. Couple the mounting concern about a mathematics course with the adjustment to college life and WOW . . . you might be facing a major momentum stopper to success at the very point of entry into a time of promise and excitement.

A Student's Guide to Math Success: Overcoming Barriers is a book written for you as you transition into college and possibly lack confidence in your mathematical ability. It can also be helpful if you are good at math but want to pick up a few tips on overcoming the stressors associated with learning. If you want to approach the study of mathematics with a stronger tool box of strategies to channel your feelings and beliefs about your ability in a positive direction, and if you want to build some basic skills, then get your pencil, something to eat, and a nice place to study. This guide will help you develop success strategies by telling real-life student stories, sharing practical tips on what to do and when, and introducing some approaches to help you build a positive, personal awareness about how to study mathematics.

ACKNOWLEDGMENTS

The authors wish to acknowledge the support and insights of the students of Immaculata University who studied mathematics during the Fall 2017 term and who shared their stories, their goals, and their hopes for success.

MATH

HOW CAN FOUR LETTERS CAUSE SO MUCH TROUBLE?

1.1: What Is Math Anxiety and What Are Its Causes?

... If I only had the nerve!

If you are reading this book, you must be facing some math course or math problem. Yes, it can be daunting if you have had poor experiences in the past. Or it could be deflating, and you feel you are stupid or not able to learn math. Or you could be convinced that math is a four-letter word for failure. Do you ever wake up in the morning and wish you could go to the Wizard of Oz and ask for the confidence to believe you can be successful ... if I only had the nerve? If only, if only ... dream on, Friend! Well, just step back for a minute to see if there is a remedy for some of your math anxiety without the intervention of the great Wizard or some magic spell.

Fear, panic, apprehension, mind-blocks all stand in the way of allowing you to start fresh at learning something new. "Math" gets a bad rap because it is both "old" and "new." If you feel that math is going to be an uphill battle for you, then you are thinking that all your past experiences will dictate your success or failure in the current situation.

But you get up each morning as a new person. You have new ideas and a fresh perspective on the day. You look forward to new encounters with your friends or learning something new or shopping at a new store or discovering a new app or mastering some new aspect of a game or sport. So why not think about math in the same way? It's a new opportunity. Give math a chance to be new for you!

Math can be a tough subject to learn and master. Oh sure, it is easy for some, but not for everyone. Admit it; each unique person can do something better than anyone else. Everyone has talents. But math … you have to know it's going to be a challenge to learn. And yes, there are strategies and practices that can help you. One of the first strategies is to know your best learning environment.

- Do you study hard things in the morning or later in the day?
- Do you like distractions in the background like music or the TV to help absorb your anxiety?
- Do you prefer to work on something technical on a full stomach or with a light snack?
- Do you need gum or candy or water nearby to keep your energy going strong?
- Do you need a hard chair, a table, a quiet space, or some place where lots of people walk by?
- Is it easier for you to write on blank paper or lined?
- Do you prefer pencil or pen?

Setting yourself up in a good environment might make your task less stressful and help you create a personal space for learning. Another strategy has to do with mental stamina. Learning math demands patience with one's own learning struggles, and it demands big-time effort and practice. Think about some things you find challenging to do—things that have required you to invest time. Everyone is different. For you it might be practicing a musical instrument, learning the rules of a sport, patiently listening to a lecture, working on a task with little help or by yourself. Are you interested in learning math? Is math success important to you? Can you find any common ideas in how you approach a task that is hard for you and transfer your approach to learning math? Sometimes it is more about making yourself want to do it than the doing itself. What would make doing math fun for you? Here's a hard question: Is your math anxiety about your attitude or your skill? Another hard question: Are you committed to your own success? Do you have the mental grit to give math a second chance?

If I only had the nerve … confidence … stamina …

Think about this: Today extreme sports are cool! The competitions are thrilling and the competitors have amazing skills and courage. Have you ever watched those athletes soar into the air from a half-pipe and then perform amazing twists and flips? They appear to have absolute confidence and total control of their boards—defying gravity. The first phase of learning how to do tricks with a skateboard involves a lot of preparation: get the helmet, get some pads, practice some basic moves like rocking back and forth in the base of the half-pipe, work on balance, and gradually ease into pumping to gain energy and increase speed. Skateboarders grow into their craft. They start out with small goals for performance, practice over and over, fall many times, get up and start again, and then ask what did I do right? What did I do wrong? How can I do better? Who can help me do better? Now you think you can do math? Probably with practice … and if you want to.

If you have been good at math and now just have a math mental block or a much harder course, then you are probably skilled at the basic craft. To grow into your craft you may need to get a little extra help with the tricky parts, or you may need to learn how to look at a problem from a different perspective. The challenge is to keep working hard and asking, "How can I do better? Who can show me how? What did I do right? What is causing my mental slow down?" Being clear with yourself about what you know, what your questions are, and when to get help can be the key to advancing your knowledge and skill in math and overcoming your fear that you cannot go to the next level.

On the other hand, if you feel as though you have never been good at math, then the lessons of the *neophyte* skateboarder may be a practical model for you. You can become easily overwhelmed if things get too hard too fast. Start by planning regular times to do math. Ask yourself: Do I need to do math with someone? Remind yourself that focused practice will help, but seek guidance if you are struggling. Know your questions and where you are stuck. Falling over and over again is not productive; doing problems over and over, making the same mistakes, isn't either. Work hard at the assignments, but make sure you study what your teacher has shared in class before you start so you are ready to practice. Sometimes it is helpful to rewrite your notes from class to be sure you follow the logic and have all the steps to a solution mapped out.

Try to think about why you are not "getting it" and where you find your mental block. Know who your best coach is: perhaps your teacher, a tutor, a friend, someone in your class. Talk to your coach. Don't mess around with learning. Math can get hard very quickly, so take the time early to ask for help and guidance. Like the skateboarders, think about what you want to accomplish, one trick at a time.

1.2: The Cycle of Frustration and Futility

M-A-T-H ... four letters that can cause so much trouble. The problem is that sometimes math is so easy and other times it is so hard. Have you heard yourself say "I got this" only to realize that while you understood something when your teacher was doing it, now that you are solo it is much more difficult? Just when you think you have the subject conquered and you are on the right path, things get so hard or complicated that it just seems unfair. Why can't math be like other subjects where you can read it and discuss it with your friends? Or finish one thing and leave it behind to learn something else with a fresh start? Or like a movie where you can watch it and remember the parts that make you happy or inspired or fascinated or satisfied? Math has so many things that you have to remember! And you have to integrate learning from one day to the next and from one semester to the next. Is math about learning for meaning or is it about calculations and answers?

Sometimes it is a frustrating cycle, and if it isn't useful then it is futile to work so hard to achieve so little.

Okay, so now what? If you identify with any of the chat in this opening paragraph or if you have heard yourself say the same things, what can you do to break the cycle of frustration and futility? Well, what about creating a mantra for yourself? When you wake up in the morning, put both feet on the floor, and think about the new day before you, repeat your mantra. Your mantra may use the inspiring words from famous figures. Do you recognize the names of the authors of the quotes which follow? Perhaps each gives you something to consider in your own attitude toward using failure, envisioning success, and being the kind of person you want to be.

> *Success consists of going from failure to failure without loss of enthusiasm.*
> *—Winston Churchill*
>
> *It's fine to celebrate success, but it is more important to heed the lessons of failure.*
> *—Bill Gates*
>
> *Nothing in life is to be feared, it is only to be understood. Now is the time to understand more, so that we may fear less.*
> *—Marie Curie*
>
> *What I am looking for is not out there, it is in me.*
> *—Helen Keller*
>
> *You must do the things you think you cannot do.*
> *—Eleanor Roosevelt*
>
> *If there is no struggle, there is no progress.*
> *—Frederick Douglass*

If none of these individuals speak to you and to your goal of success in math, why not try Google to find your own mantra. A mantra can contain just a few meaningful words, such as: "Keep climbing!" Perhaps the message of a contemporary singer might appeal to you or a current or historical political leader or a religious spokesperson. Or maybe you want to find a superhero who will inspire you or an icon which will send you a message of perseverance and drive. Take your mantra to heart so that your mindset will be one of success and positive energy. Make a poster; use it as your screensaver; write it on your math book (if you own the book). You can turn around your attitude toward math and then start building a positive foundation for learning. M-A-T-H = Make A Turn Happen!

How simple is this? A friend, RT, was recently chatting about his experiences in learning math and his career. Okay, so he liked math in grade school, but his advice about what matters in life and learning seem really relevant here. He moved from working in a field where he tested electrical engines to being a computer technician. And RT said that many questions arise every day in the computer business which he has never encountered. The best thing to do is: 1) look for someone who knows more than you do and ask; 2) go to the Internet and search for a YouTube video or site which will provide insight into your question. The very first step, however, is to know your question. The next thing RT said was you have to want to learn; you have to spend time working at things. Own your learning. That is what will serve you best in life, so it is more than just learning "math," rather learning math can offer you the opportunity to create success techniques for your personal lifelong learning strategy. Why not stop and write down in the box in Figure 1.1 one technique that is a part of your personal learning strategy.

Figure 1.1

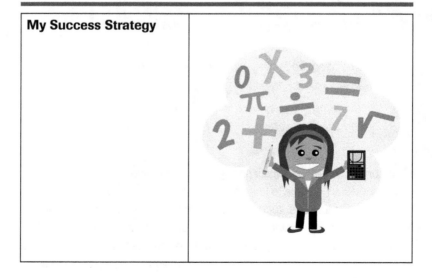

My Success Strategy

You are amazing, you know! Here you are worried about being successful in math, having homework and a new course to face, and yet you are reading this self-help book. This suggests you are really committed to learning and succeeding. Okay, now look for a moment at the emotional side of math. If you have not been successful in the past, you may have a deep-seated feeling of failure. And failure hurts. A first step might be to acknowledge that hurt and sense of emotion associated with your past experiences, and ask yourself if you are ready to move on. Here are some questions to ponder:

- Is math your stumbling block, or is it learning things you have to remember?
- Is math your nemesis, or is it learning something without foundational skills?
- Is math your problem, or is it learning something you cannot break into small pieces?
- Is math your Waterloo, or is it learning things that require sequencing?
- Is math your greatest challenge, or can you figure out what aspect of learning math causes you the most trouble? Name it.

Thomas Edison supposedly failed 10,000 times before finding the key to making a light bulb work. He thought about each failure as a stepping stone to understanding. It is fun to think about Edison and the invention of the "light bulb" since that image is often used to reference waking up to some new insight. Just as Edison and many other movers and shakers have shared, it is not the failure that matters but what you learn from the failed attempt.

Dealing with negative feelings can be an important aspect of beginning a journey toward learning. Sometimes an advisor is the best person with whom to talk so you can get ideas about what is causing your reactions and then work to resolve those feelings. Sometimes a tutor can be a valuable resource because a tutor can give additional guidance on creating success techniques, which are individualized to your needs and will help to rebuild your confidence. Often a teacher can provide out-of-class assistance pinpointing your areas in need of improvement or places where you are successful. Being with people who are positive about learning can foster a sense of community and encouragement.

If you hear yourself saying, "I can't get THIS," then it is the critical moment to start thinking, "THIS cannot get me!" In *The Wizard of Oz*, the recurring theme was "if only … "—if I only had a heart, if I only had a brain, if I only had the nerve. Each character was very clear about what he needed to achieve his personal goal. The shift in thinking moved from I cannot do this because … to I can do this if … . Being positive, looking for the right help, and moving in the direction of growth will set you on the path to a new beginning in your encounter with math. So get ready to ask your teacher well-formulated questions.

1.3: What Does the Research Tell You? You Are Not Alone!

Research shows that there are many people who have negative feelings and beliefs about their ability to learn mathematics or who simply struggle to learn mathematics. That is good for you because you know you are not alone! Learning mathematics can be a daunting task when you have limited time to invest in each subject or a shaky background in the basics. Because it is SO challenging to SO many folks, there are lots of tools, websites, and other resources to support you in learning. That's the good news about the math itself.

Anxiety and fear are also well-researched emotions. So what does the research say about overcoming these momentum stoppers? Well, there is no easy answer, but one idea is to find the unique combination of mental strategies that will keep you going in a positive direction when these emotions well up. Rather than starting with an attitude of self-defeat, begin with a growth mindset.

Athletes can become derailed by thinking about missing a shot in basketball, striking out with bases loaded, or throwing an interception in a tie game! To refocus the athlete on personal performance, sports psychology suggests envisioning what "winning" looks like. Learning mathematics has elements of playing a game also: there are rules to follow, skills to be acquired, strategies to employ in different situations, tests of ability. Envisioning yourself as a winner offers a way to channel your energies in a positive direction. So what does winning look like for you? Aim high, but not unrealistically. Be realistic about your goals. Visualize the outcome you hope to attain. Make a recording of how you will approach your assignment, test, or next class. Be specific about what you hope to accomplish, with whom you will speak, how you will formulate questions, what you will say to the instructor. Play the recording over to yourself as you prepare. Take the time to acknowledge your feelings and turn on the self-talk tape, mimicking your recording of success. This strategy will put you in the company of many successful athletes, actors, performers, and leaders.

In case you thought you were the first student embarking on a journey to college with apprehension about mathematics, listen up and take heart by hearing the voices of a few students who tell their stories. Like you, at one point in their lives, they wouldn't rank math in their all-time top 50 list of fun things to do. You shouldn't be shocked—lots of students enter college with strong feelings of apprehension and anxiety about math, but they still manage to do quite well in the subject. See if your experiences are similar to these students' experiences.

VOICES FROM CAMPUS 1.1

Rachel

Frustration from First Grade Forward

I went to public school from kindergarten through fifth grade, where it seemed to me that no one cared how you did in math. My progress was average, at best, and so was my basic understanding of the concepts. When I transferred to Catholic school in sixth grade, I was way behind all of the other students in my class. I mean, WAY BEHIND!!! As a way to help me to get caught up, my parents sent me to tutoring, but honestly, that just made me feel dumb, and my grades didn't improve. So I stopped trying, and I gave up hope that I'd ever be good at math. I convinced myself that I would NEVER be good at math. My parents were frustrated, and eventually they gave up on their efforts to help me.

YOUR TURN 1.1

Directions: Put Rachel's story on pause for a moment. Be honest with yourself. Do you believe that the ability to do math is only for "math-gifted" students? If so, do you believe that without that "gift" you'll never be good at math? Why do you believe it? Write down your answers to these questions.

Now continue with Rachel's story.

VOICES FROM CAMPUS 1.2

Rachel (continued)

I like one thing about math—the challenge of finding an answer to a problem. The notion that the answer is out there somewhere intrigues me—it really does. But my experiences with the subject from grade school on through middle school just reinforced my belief that even though there is always a definite answer to the problem that is posed, I'm just not good enough at the subject to get to it, no matter how hard I try. Once I reached that realization, I stopped trying.

YOUR TURN 1.2

Directions: But wait! Rachel likes the challenge of finding an answer to a problem! She knows there is an answer to the math problem! She just can't find it! Can you recall when you were close to solving a problem yet the solution seemed just out of reach? Create an emoji representing the frustration of not being able to find the solution.

Can you empathize with Rachel? Maybe your frustrations and anxieties related to math have their roots in your elementary school years, too. Sometimes, elementary teachers might really love their jobs and enjoy the challenges of working with students and helping them learn, but these same teachers might unknowingly contribute to their students' math anxiety.

Maybe your teachers' explanations just didn't connect with you. So you believe that math and you do not compute!

However, some teachers do a good job promoting an understanding of math and can also provide strategies for solving problems that build their students' confidence. When you encounter good elementary teachers, it gives you a slight edge—you grow up believing that you can do math. And guess what? Like many things in life, it becomes a self-fulfilling prophecy—you believe that you can do it, so you extend your effort and minimize your doubts and, *voila*, you can do it!

Okay, so what do you do if you never had a teacher who made math make sense for you? Some students who experience frustrations and anxieties related to mathematics overcome those anxieties and proceed to excel in the subject. Granted, it takes a serious shift in attitude—going from doubting one's abilities to being confident in one's abilities. Some students get help from other people: their peers, their professors or teachers, or maybe a support group or study group.

Suppose that Rachel was that skateboarder from earlier in the chapter. Do you think that she'd have defined HER successes based on what other skateboarders were doing? Probably not! But when it came to her math skills and confidence, that's exactly what she wound up doing. She decided that her classmates were ALL better than she was, and no matter how hard she tried (remember all of those trips to the tutor!), she couldn't become successful like her classmates.

There's no doubt about it, it's not easy to struggle with any skill while those around you are seemingly all doing better than you are. But do you really think that Lebron James measures his successes on the court based on what someone else is doing? In all likelihood, he works on his own skills—complete with frustrations and failures—until he refines his game, and his successes are evident. You see, to be good (or even great) takes GRIT. Rachel has math ability—make no mistake about that! Unfortunately, she's caught up in past struggles, and she focuses on how her skills compare to her peers' skills. Rachel can succeed. She has the resident skill set and is even intrigued that the answer is out there somewhere. What's missing is grit—a willingness to commit to success—a willingness to work hard and savor HER successes, without feeling the need to compare herself to others. Rachel just needs to do HER OWN THING! Remember, like the skateboarder, a student who enjoys success in math exhibits mental stamina, patience, resilience, and a willingness to exert a big effort—that is true GRIT!

And you can be sure there are people who experienced math anxiety and overcame it and achieved success—they're not extinct like T. Rexes (and no, they don't have those short stubby arms either). By the way, how does a T. Rex eat pizza?

Figure 1.2

Take a look at Armando's story. He overcame his fear of math, and today he is well on his way to achieving great success in the subject.

VOICES FROM CAMPUS 1.3

Armando
From Frustrated to Fantastic

I was labeled as "weak in math" by one of my teachers very early on in elementary school, and I think this label really became a self-fulfilling prophecy for me. I just accepted the fact that I would never be good at math because it was hard for me. I struggled in math all throughout middle school, and I honestly hated it. I thought math was impossible.

Everything changed for me when I went to a week-long math camp the summer before I started high school. My teacher was very encouraging, and he showed me that I could be good at math if I put in the effort to understand the concepts. He made math fun and broke things down in ways that made so much sense to me. I am so glad that I attended that math camp! The camp gave me the opportunity to review the math concepts that had always confused me in an environment where I felt comfortable asking for help.

When I started high school, I decided to approach math with a positive attitude and open mind. This mindset made all the difference for me, and I started to excel in math because I stopped viewing it as my worst subject. When my math classes got hard, I did not give up. I sought out extra help from my teachers, and I printed out practice worksheets for the concepts that confused me the most. Before each test, I also created study sheets on which I would write out important concepts and example problems in all different colors. These study sheets were great study tools for me.

Shifting my approach to math truly changed everything. I realized that I had to approach math as I would any other subject. I knew there would be difficult concepts, but I also knew that I could succeed if I dedicated time to the subject and asked for extra help when I needed it. Ever since I changed my attitude, math has become one of my best subjects, and now I really enjoy it.

Armando exemplifies the idea that a change in attitude about mathematics can be ignited by something outside a math class or tutoring center. For him, it was a week-long math camp. Now, you might be muttering under your breath, "There's NO WAY that I'd ever head to a week-long camp where we study math. Nope. No thanks. Not my idea of a fun camp outing! You go ahead to math camp; I'll just sit here and eat a s'more!"

Figure 1.3

Give Armando credit for his willingness to step outside of his normal routine and comfort zone. And remember that his normal routine included an aversion toward math and a frustration factor fueled by his teachers labeling him as "not good at math."

In his case, it took a change in geography along with a patient, kind instructor, willing to answer his questions to serve as the trigger of Armando's changed attitude toward mathematics. Equally significant was the recognition that hard work on his part could yield the outcomes that he desired, rather than the outcomes that he previously dreaded—low test scores and a lack of confidence in his abilities in mathematics.

You're already making the change in geography; you're leaving your high school mathematics classroom and heading off to college. It's the perfect opportunity to separate yourself from the anxiety that you've felt toward math and embark on a new path. With a new mindset and hard work on your part, your success in mathematics is possible, just like Armando's. Find a study partner, look for your college's math center, inquire about a student tutor, or just refocus your energies in a positive light, and prepare to "allow" yourself to succeed in math. And most importantly, face the challenge of conquering your math anxiety by believing that your ability to do math is not a predetermined trait. You can do it!

YOUR TURN 1.3

Armando refers to his change in "mindset." Here are two definitions for you to think about:

1. **Fixed Mindset**—you believe your abilities are carved in stone and can never change.
2. **Growth Mindset**—you believe that your abilities are things you cultivate through your efforts, your strategies, and help from others.

These definitions are from a great book entitled *Mindset* by Carol S. Dweck, Ph.D.

Dr. Dweck (2006) states that an individual can move from a "fixed mindset" to a "growth mindset." Armando made the shift from a "fixed mindset" to a "growth mindset." This is what made a difference in Armando's academic life. This experience will also make a difference in Armando's future professional and personal endeavors.

Which definition do you most associate with and why? This is a hard question. Take some time to think about it for now. We'll come back to this a bit later.

The next student success story is from Desiree. Again, this is the story of a student who experienced frustration in mathematics at a young age. It seems that Desiree's teacher was a proponent of having students solve problems on the board. Don't get this wrong; some students love going to the board and demonstrating their skills in front of the teacher and their classmates. Surely, when students struggle at the board, the input and feedback from a caring teacher can assist and bolster student confidence. Unfortunately, for many students, instead of receiving kind assistance that aids their understanding, these "board sessions" amplify their feelings of incompetence and foster their anxiety about math. Can you identify with Desiree's experience?

VOICES FROM CAMPUS 1.4

Desiree

Get Me Away from This Board!

I was never a strong math student. I understood the concepts within basic math, Algebra 1 and Algebra 2, and even trigonometry. But when my teacher would call on me for an answer to a homework problem or would send me to the board, it was as if my whole life flashed before my eyes. I haven't had the most luck with math teachers in elementary and middle school. I think this was the basis of my problem. I vividly remember more than three of my math teachers in my younger years refusing to help me, or just giving me the 'go back to your seat' hand wave while never looking up from their cell phone when I asked for help.

In high school, the phobia stalled; it didn't go away, but it wasn't as prevalent. It would come and go, depending on the day and what I was learning. When I was leaning toward a science- and math-based field, I knew this phobia had to permanently end. So on my very first day as a college student, I sat in my very first college math class ever, and I promised myself this stress and nervousness would end. I was extremely lucky; because of my professor's style and energy, my anxiety of even thinking about math was gone within a week or two.

I would feel sick to my stomach when thinking about attending math classes in my previous years of education. Maturity and finding a comfortable connection with a professional has made all of the difference to me as a growing individual.

Okay you're probably thinking Desiree got a good teacher, but in my life, I've been stuck with the lousy ones! That's not the reason for her newfound successes in math. She determined that she needed to change her attitude toward math, but more importantly, she determined that she COULD change those attitudes and perceptions about the subject. The beautiful thing about Desiree's story is that without the change in perspective about math, she'd most likely have continued to struggle in the math courses required for a science major. Sure, the teacher probably helped to curb her fears about math; however, her successes on tests and quizzes aided her in changing her notion that she wasn't able to succeed in math. Instead of being paralyzed by fear that she MIGHT not be able to do the math, she applied herself to the fullest. And guess what! She conquered her fears and vanquished that ugly monster called mathematics!

Both Armando and Desiree tried a different approach. They allowed a new start to be a springboard to success and stopped looking back at past struggles and difficulties. Their efforts in math show tremendous personal growth. Like the skateboarder mentioned before, both of these students developed plans to succeed. They started with small goals for improvement and subsequently practiced over and over. They determined where they could go when they needed guidance, and they sought assistance when needed.

You see, math anxiety isn't really just about being able to "do the math." Really, for most people who've developed some anxiety about math, it's the "fear" that they won't be successful or the "fear" that their grades won't be As and Bs that paralyzes them and won't even allow them to attempt to be successful in math. Rachel, Armando, and Desiree all had elementary experiences that convinced them that they were not good at mathematics. More importantly, their perceptions about their abilities in math led them to dread the subject and aided in their development of math anxiety. But both Armando and Desiree have moved past the anxiety that they once felt about math, and they have been earning good grade after good grade in challenging college-level math classes. For these two individuals, it took a willingness to approach math with a more "can do" attitude and a willingness to invest themselves in learning.

Now try something different. In fact, try two things: 1) figure out the source of your math anxiety and then 2) determine your mindset.

Did someone in your family or an elementary teacher play a key role in your perception that you aren't good at math? Here is an exercise to try. During your academic career, many people send you messages—some positive and some negative. For now, focus your energies on the negatives. Yeah, you're going to be a glass half empty person! Don't worry though, before long, you'll explore ways to turn that frown upside down.

See if you can complete the following chart by entering messages that you might have received from someone about your abilities to learn (maybe the subject was math, but maybe it was another subject).

YOUR TURN 1.4

Message Inventory and Source

Example Messages:

- You're not as good at this as your brother/sister was.
- You're so slow with your calculations. Why can't you speed things up?
- You'd better stick to Shakespeare—maybe write a nice sonnet.
- Can't you hurry up? I need to make dinner.

Directions: Okay, now it's your turn. List some messages that you've heard about your abilities in math, and also determine who sent you the message. Yes, you're going to take a look at who has played a key role in helping you to develop your anxieties regarding math.

Message	Who sent or sends you that message?

Now, look at those messages and see who the senders are. It's possible that they came from someone other than you, and you just internalized them. That's not unusual. You see, from when you were young, you learned to "respect your elders" and that with age they've attained wisdom. Okay, that's kind of rich; you've met many people who might be older but sure wouldn't be confused with Einstein! Sure, some people contribute insights that are meaningful, well thought out, and truly helpful. Others, however, simply say things without the least bit of thought regarding how their statements will be received and internalized.

The point of this exercise is just this: If you've "learned" these feelings from external input, you can also unlearn them. Remember, YOU control what goes on inside that head of yours!

Think about it: Like Armando, Desiree changed her "mindset." Carol Dwek (2006), gives the expanded definitions of two types of mindset. She explains:

1. **Fixed Mindset:** You believe your abilities are carved in stone—can never change. You concentrate on the skills you can perform successfully. You demonstrate those skills repeatedly. You never have the confidence to attempt learning new skills because you are not confident you will be successful.

2. **Growth Mindset:** You believe that you cultivate your abilities through your efforts, your strategies, and help from others. You always "stretch" yourself by attempting to learn new skills. When you are not successful, you go back and try again until you are successful.

Okay, so now that you know how to differentiate fixed mindset and growth mindset, explore a little activity that is designed to help you to determine your mindset regarding math and your skill in the subject. Of course, it's important to realize that mindset isn't poured in concrete; it is surely able to evolve and change. Two of our student contributors are examples of a changed mindset. Both Armando and Desiree have progressed to a growth mindset, and their current success in math is due in part to their change in attitude and mindset.

Armando and Desiree both changed their mindsets about their math ability. Both of these students saw a shift to a "growth mindset." Spend some time and try to determine your mindset about math—is yours fixed or growth?

YOUR TURN 1.5

Determining Your Mindset Directions

Directions: Consider each of the prompts below and choose the response that most accurately reflects your level of agreement with the statement. Use the responses TWIS (Strongly Agree), TT (Agree), NW (Disagree), or YCBS (Strongly Disagree).

TWIS—That's What I'm Saying (I Strongly Agree)
TT—True That (I Agree)
NW—No Way! (I Disagree)
YCBS—You Can't Be Serious (I Strongly Disagree)

Go ahead—fill in the bubble that best reflects your feeling about each statement. Then take a look at whether your mindset is fixed or growth. Feel free to break out those new spiffy colored pencils or pens that you bought for back to school and go for it!

No.	Statement	TWIS	TT	NW	YCBS
1	My math ability cannot improve.	◯	◯	◯	◯
2	Some people are born with mathematical minds; I'm just not one of them.	◯	◯	◯	◯
3	I'm not good at math because my parents weren't good at math.	◯	◯	◯	◯
4	There's no room for creativity or imagination in doing math.	◯	◯	◯	◯
5	I won't get it, no matter how much time I spend on it.	◯	◯	◯	◯
6	If you can't solve a problem in a few minutes, you should give up.	◯	◯	◯	◯
7	Math mainly involves a lot of memorization, formulas, and facts.	◯	◯	◯	◯
8	All of the math that I need I can do on my calculator.	◯	◯	◯	◯

Now, try to come up with a score that you can use to determine whether your responses indicate a fixed mindset or a growth mindset. Give yourself four points for each TWIS, three points for each TT, two points for each NW, and one point for each YCBS. You can use your calculator, if you want! Fill in your total score here: _____.

Examine your score. If your score is between 8 and 16, you exhibit a pretty strong growth mindset. Good news for you—success in math can be had by applying yourself. Just like our friend the skateboarder, you can plan, practice, fail—oh, you'll fail (not many successes occur before innumerable failures)—and ultimately, you can chart a path to success in mathematics. If your score is between 16 and 24, you're more of a fixed mindset person. Now there's nothing wrong with that; it's what you believe right now. But remember, life is full of changes, and attitude is one of the things that you CAN change if you set your mind to doing so. For now, why not agree that you'll read the rest of this book, think about the points that are made, and maybe be willing to explore a new course of action regarding your feelings about math. If your score is between 24 and 32, you're pretty much a "hard core" fixed mindset person. Again, that's fine—it's how you feel right now. Hey, at least you were honest. You didn't select other answers because you felt that other students would have chosen them. Kudos and congrats to you for that!

Now reflect for a couple of minutes on something in your life that you are proud to have attained or accomplished. Maybe you are a skateboarder and you've mastered the art of the 720 Gazelle Flip—eat your heart out, Tony Hawk! Maybe you led your baseball team to a league championship with a .500 batting average—eat your heart out, Bryce Harper! Maybe your apple pie won a blue ribbon at the state fair—eat your heart out, Betty Crocker! Even if none of these three situations quite describe you, you've succeeded at something due to your perseverance, effort, and willingness to work through failure and frustration. So you see, you have exhibited growth mindset traits in other aspects of your life. Read this book, think about what you've read, and be willing to consider changing your mindset about your math abilities. You can do it!

Credits

CHAPTER

2

WHY SHOULD I CARE ABOUT DOING WELL IN MATH?

2.1: Imagining Your Future Self

Can you imagine yourself in the future? Pause your present life for a moment and play with your imagination. Do you see yourself as an executive for some tech company? A well-regarded artist? A sportscaster? Perhaps a carpenter, accountant, lawyer, sales clerk, homemaker, astronaut, construction worker, bank teller, or media marketer! Have you ever heard yourself ask, "Why do I have to learn all this stuff in math? I will never use it"?

Be honest. Do you know every detail of your future life? Do you know every skill or resource you will need to use to land a better job, capitalize on a great deal, or take advantage of an unexpected opportunity? Well, you know the famous saying of Dr. Louis Pasteur, who back in 1854 apparently voiced these words, "Fortune favors the prepared mind." The range of people giving advice on using the present moment to prepare for a future good is limitless. Just pop the phrase "prepared mind" into your search engine and you will find that preparing for an undiscovered future time is repeated in thousands of ways. Here are a few more recent proponents of preparing your mind for the opportunity yet to be revealed. What they say might resonate with your way of thinking:

> "Opportunity does not waste time with those who are unprepared" (Koyenikan,2016).
>
> "Every action in the present prepares us for the future" (Akita, 2014).

According to the Bureau of Labor Statistics (BLS, 2015), the number of jobs an individual will hold over a lifetime is increasing. In one report, BLS indicated that an average worker holds 4 jobs by the time he or she reaches 32 years of age and should prepare for at least 10 to 12 jobs over a career. That prediction certainly should encourage those working on a college degree to develop as many skills and accumulate as much knowledge as possible. The message is clear: The more prepared you are, the more likely you will be ready to meet future opportunity. Math skills are used in every walk of life.

Can you avoid using basic math in a job? Your answer should be a resounding "NO." Math is everywhere from making simple calculations, to estimating answers with numbers, to using formulae in an Excel spreadsheet. Employers today are looking for applicants who know how to use a spreadsheet. Yes, spreadsheets are rooted in math! Spreadsheets use cells to hold information, which in math lingo are just variables of a different name. Artists, contractors, engineers, and choreographers all use geometry. So do interior designers or simple homeowners when purchasing the right size carpet or looking to build a deck. As you might guess, being able to estimate special relationships is important; you can build these skills in geometry.

Basic math knowledge forms a foundation for future learning of concepts, logical thinking, and integration of ideas. It should be no surprise that computers, phones, networks, in fact, all life in a digital world will depend more and more on fundamental math concepts. So learning math may be a determining factor in what role you will play in the emerging world of work. Savvy technology users who understand how things work will have an advantage whether as teachers, technicians, consultants, or consumers.

Math can be frustrating to learn. So it is important to take slow, consistent steps to get the hang of it even if you have tried many times before. You might be saying to yourself that you do not expect to unlock the mysteries of the solar system or invent the next generation of rockets. But realistically, you will be a member of a global society using the tools of the future while being an ordinary person calculating the interest on your loan, paying your credit card debt, baking a cake, or estimating the amount of a tip in a restaurant.

Math concepts are the building blocks helping you to develop logical thinking. Did you know that some research suggests that people with little math understanding are more likely to invest, save, and spend based on their emotions rather than rational thinking? Typically these people also fail to understand how debt mounts exponentially because they do not know how to calculate compound interest. On the other hand, "a study by the RAND Corporation, a nonprofit think tank, showed a direct correlation between numeracy (a fancy word for math skills), delayed recall (the ability to remember something you've seen after some delay) and your future wealth" (Hull, 2012). Some basic math knowledge might help your logic to direct your choices. So many aspects of everyday life are based in math. You do not have to love it, but you might want to appreciate its power and potential to help you be successful throughout your life. And the rewards will be great if you have less debt, more options, and a broader set of skills.

2.2: Breaking the Cycle of Frustration

Okay, now you see that math is important and you actually understand the importance. But the truth remains that math is still hard, frustrating, and time-consuming. James's story might sound familiar to you.

VOICES FROM CAMPUS 2.1

James
Scary Steps

My teachers always ask me why I dislike math. Yes, I have a negative view of math. I want to be more positive, but I have no confidence. It's hard to start problems and I can never figure out the steps. How do you break a problem into steps when you have no idea what steps to use? And when I can start a problem, I'm always afraid I'm doing the problem the wrong way. I always assume the problem is wrong since I've been wrong more than I've been right. When I'm in class, I have a fear of being called on to answer a question. I can't answer questions because I'm always a few steps behind the teacher. At that point, I'm totally overwhelmed. I also don't know how to study for math, but honestly I don't want to study since I know I won't get the right answer. I know my attitude makes things worse. If I could only be more positive ... but I don't know how.

James thought about being more positive and just did not know how to get over the hump of frustration. You're probably also wondering what you can do to rid yourself of the frustration you have with math. Before you read some suggestions for breaking your cycle of frustration, take a bit of time to answer the questions in Your Turn 2.1.

YOUR TURN 2.1

Part 1

1. What puzzles you the most about mathematics?
2. What makes you believe you can't do math?
3. Does math scare you? If so, why does it scare you? (No need to be scared! If you use a pencil, you can always erase the scary part!)
4. What type of math problems do you dislike and why? (Be specific.)
5. When you get stuck on a problem, what do you do?

Now you have thought about what makes math hard, what you like and dislike, what makes you believe you can't do math, and how you handle it when you're stuck. What will you do? Try this: Based on your answers, write a letter to your Genie asking for the characteristics you need to become a great mathematician (Your Turn 2.2).

Part 2

Imagine the following: You have been given a Genie who will grant you three wishes. (It's a fairy-tale activity, but your imagination can help develop your mindset if you make your wishes specific and genuine.) Think: Here is the urn and inside is the Genie. Write a letter to your Genie asking for two characteristics that you think would make you a great mathematician. (Save the third wish!)

There are two personal characteristics that, if developed, will help you succeed at any activity, including math. These characteristics are: GRIT and GROWTH MINDSET.

What is "grit"? Travis Bradberry (2015) defines "grit" as follows:

> Grit is that "extra something" that separates the most suc-cessful people from the rest. It's the passion, perseverance, and stamina that we must channel in order to stick with our dreams until they become a reality.

So according to Travis Bradberry (2015) grit is a combination of persever-ance, stamina, and passion. As you learn how these three characteristics lead to success you will recognize how they positively affect the problem-solving process. (Much more will be shared about problem solving in an upcoming section.)

But back to grit! Grit is a kind of super power. When combined, per-severance, stamina, and passion can act like a catapult and hurl you in the direction of success. Getting pointed in the direction of success is the first step! So how do you take that first step in the right direction?

2.3: Pointing in the Direction of Success

Use a pencil and have an eraser handy! Then push the pencil. "Push the pencil" means *you own the problem*. Don't let the problem own you. A math problem is only a combination of words and numbers on a page. You begin owning the problem by *organizing your work*. One approach is:

1. List the information that is stated directly in the problem.
2. Compute information you can determine by using the information that was stated directly.
3. Compile aspects of the problem that you do not understand (i.e., questions you need to ask your instructor or tutor).
4. Draw a picture representing the problem if it makes sense to do that.
5. State/predict what you think your answer should look like.

At this point, you haven't attempted to solve the problem; you are assuring yourself that you can begin the problem by organizing the information into a format that will assist you in getting to a solution. NOTE: You are getting to **a** solution, not necessarily **the correct** solution! Hold that thought! You will come back to this shortly.

2.4: Perseverance

Success in mathematics is about persevering. Recall that perseverance is a component of grit. So what does it mean to persevere? Newt Gingrich (Gingrich, Bernstein, & Bernstein, 1995) defines perseverance as "the hard work you do after you get tired of doing the hard work you already did."

Organizing information to gain an understanding of the problem takes time and patience. You may sometimes need to reorganize the information after your initial organization. Why? Well, after initially setting the problem up, you may see a better way to lay out information. This work helps you gain a deeper understanding of the problem. Here's a secret to problem-solving! Taking the time to organize information (and reorganize it, if necessary) in a format that makes sense will allow you to better understand what you need to solve as well as how to solve it! But you need to persevere through this step! Most students try to skip this step and go directly to a formula or equation and try to solve the problem immediately! The best mathematicians are excellent at organizing the information and asking questions about the problem prior to beginning the process of solving the problem. That's how a mathematician knows how to proceed!

2.5: Stamina

Stamina is another component of grit. The English Oxford Dictionary (2017) defines stamina as the "ability to sustain prolonged physical or mental effort." Potentially, it will take you multiple tries to get the solution to a problem! Don't worry—that's normal! Even the best mathematicians (and that includes your teachers) don't always get the correct answer on the first try! So you will need stamina to sustain you during the problem-solving process. Now is the time to think a little more deeply about "getting to the answer."

You need to gain a new perspective with regard to focusing on "getting the correct answer." No one will deny that everyone wants to be correct. However, one can compute a correct answer but not thoroughly understand why the answer is correct. Now consider this: When you get an incorrect answer and you take the time to understand why the answer is incorrect, you grow in your knowledge and understanding of the problem. The scientific method teaches that you learn from your mistakes by systematically studying the error. An error affords you the chance to learn where the approach went wrong and, more importantly, why that particular approach didn't work. Your error can be considered a success because you gained an understanding of why a particular approach did not work. Understanding why an approach did not work is just as important as knowing why an approach is successful.

But how does this relate to stamina? Assuming you take to heart the scientific method with regard to learning, you will need to increase your stamina. Just as a marathon runner needs to build up the physical endurance to sustain running for 26 miles, you too will need to build up your stamina for enduring multiple attempts at solving a problem. This brings you to the third component of grit: passion.

2.6: Passion

Passion will probably be the toughest characteristic for you to adopt, especially if you DO NOT like math! How does someone who doesn't like math develop a passion for math? No one can initially convince you to develop an enthusiasm for math. However, you can develop a growth mindset. Travis Bradberry (2015) states:

> Common sense would suggest that having ability, like being smart, inspires confidence. It does, but only while the going is easy. The deciding factor in life is how you handle setbacks and challenges. People with a growth mindset welcome setbacks with open arms.

Based on the assumption that you've read this far in this book, you have a desire to improve your academic performance in math. Without a positive mindset for handling setbacks and redoing work, the characteristics of perseverance and stamina will be difficult for you to sustain.

In her book, *Grit: The Power of Passion and Perseverance*, Angela Duckworth (2016) provides language that promotes a growth mindset. Consider the following statements from her book and consider how your attitude would change if you heard these statements about your work:

You're a learner, I love that.
That didn't work. Let's talk about how you approached it and what might work better.
Great job! What's the one thing that could have been even better?
This is hard. Don't feel bad if you can't do it yet.
I have high standards. I'm holding you to them because I know we can reach them together. (Duckworth, 2016, p. 182)

Reflect on these statements. All of the statements provide hope! In addition to hope, these statements are encouraging you to reach further—to not be satisfied with your current performance. The combination of hope and not being satisfied with your performance added to perseverance and stamina will lead to an improved performance. And it just might lead you to develop a passion for problem-solving!

YOUR TURN 2.3

Part 3

Develop a personal mantra that combines the ideas about grit and a growth mindset so that you will have a reminder to apply grit and a growth mindset to your study of math.

Here's a sample mantra which combines the characteristics of grit into a mathematical equation:

PERSEVERANCE + STAMINA + GROWTH MINDSET = IMPROVED PERFORMANCE

Hey! Makes sense to form an equation, doesn't it? After all, this is a book about math stuff and life.

MATH MAKES SENSE

DOES YOUR ANSWER?

3.1: Are My Answers Sensible?
Number Sense

How many times have you been asked, "What do you want to be when you grow up?" Do you hear other people say energetically, "a mathematician"? Probably not. Many folks, possibly including you, ask the question "When am I ever going to use this?" But still, face the fact that most people do use math regularly in their daily life. Uncertainty about the future usefulness of some information may not be the best criterion for determining what to learn in the present. Your career path is unknown. Math might be very important to your future success. Some math concepts will fit well into your toolbox of understanding. The most basic might be called "number sense."

When are you going to use number sense in the real world? That's easy to answer: in a store for understanding a bargain; at a game, appreciating sports stats; at the ATM, checking to see if you have enough cash …

Figure 3.1

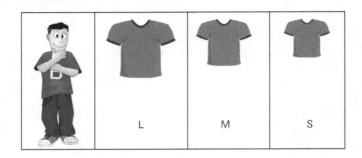

L   M   S

Beyond that, learning to estimate an answer or determine the reasonableness of an answer helps you to know if the details of your calculations lead to the anticipated answer; if not, then you'd better check the details. Here are some basic concepts related to estimation of answers.

Reasonableness of an answer is generally related to the context of the question. Sometimes people refer to a ballpark guess. This means you need to think about a range where the answer might fall. You can ask yourself: Based on what I know, is this answer too big or too small?

In the figure 3.1, Randy is trying to buy a shirt for someone. Should he buy small, medium, or large? You should ask a lot of questions. Is he buying the shirt for himself or someone else? (This is the context.) How big are the shirts? (These are the math facts.) Can he measure the size of the shirt with someone of similar size? (This will create a model for his guess and add to his insights.) He chooses "large." (This is his guess based on the context, math facts, and comparison with other concepts, all of which contribute to his understanding.)

Estimating an answer sometimes involves making the numbers easier to manage in your head. Rounding the number up or down so the digit in the *units* column is a zero can be helpful. The *units* column is the digit immediately to the left of the decimal point or hanging on the end of a number if there is no decimal point. For example, in the number 1205, the *units* column contains the 5. In the number 120.5, the *units* column contains the 0.

Here's a problem and a "guess-timate." Add 33 and 76. To make the mental math easier, change 33 to 30 so you have a zero in the *units* column. You would say the answer is "about" 106. (Exact answer is 109.) Here's another problem with a "guess-timate." Multiply 12 times $4.99. Well, $4.99

Figure 3.2

is close to $5.00 so move it closer to $5. That makes it easier to estimate that the answer is $60. Or we could change the 12 to 10 and multiply, yielding $49.90. One estimate is high and the other low. Mental math helps you to put complex pieces together in your head.

YOUR TURN 3.1

Number Sense

What would you do with the following information to get a guess-timate?

Number	Operation	Number	Estimate	Thought process?
57	+ (add)	72	About 130	
88	X (multiply)	$2.98	About $270	
36	/ (divide)	15	About 2	

When you are estimating, you have a lot of freedom; you can experiment with what makes calculation easier for you. It is true you cannot just forget everything you know about the basic operations of add, subtract, multiply, and divide, nor can you blow off the rules of the crazy world of fractions. But you can build upon those basic ideas to make an educated guess. Educated guessing means you use everything you know, make the calculations a bit easier, and try to project a range where the answer will fall.

Do not be afraid to experiment or ask others about how they estimate an answer. Everyone has some shopping tricks or guess-timate strategies. Ask: What's my guess? Does my actual answer come close to the guess? Why does my answer make sense? Oh, and yes, you need to use your brain at each stage. Educated guessing is a thinking game.

3.2: A Primer on Rules for Signed Numbers

Anyone who has studied algebra is aware of signed numbers. Adding, subtracting, multiplying, and dividing signed numbers can be confusing because the sign of the number plays a role in the answer. So doing an operation correctly involves a calculation. It's just like working with whole numbers (all the positive numbers) and giving consideration to the sign on the number.

Signed numbers are useful because they can symbolically denote negative concepts—quantities such as a debt, a loss, the opposite. Once you understand the concept of negative quantities, then you will want to be able to calculate using them. So there are "rules of the game" for how you "play" when signed numbers are used. You can lay down white and black cards to visually represent a positive number (white) and a negative number (black). When you see a negative quantity, you write a negative sign (−) in front of the number. When you have a positive quantity, you write a positive sign (+) in front of the number. If no sign appears, then the number is considered positive. The number 0 has no sign; it is not considered positive or negative.

So how does this work when adding? Combining (adding) three positives and two positives = five positives. In Figure 3.3 you see three white cards and in Figure 3.4 you see two white cards; combined you will have five white cards. You write $3 + 2 = 5$. Easy!

Figure 3.3

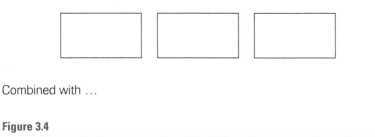

Combined with ...

Figure 3.4

In Figure 3.5, you see a row containing three black cards, so write -3 to represent the top row.

Figure 3.5

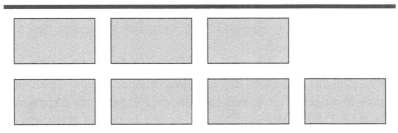

The second row contains four black cards, so write -4. When you combine (add) the two rows together you see seven black cards, which is written as −7. Black cards are designated as negative. There are seven cards, so write −7 cards or −3 + (−4) = −7. Put parentheses around the number following the plus (−4) because you want to hold together the four black cards in the second row. Parentheses act like containers to hold quantities together.

Now what do you do when you combine negatives and positives? Everyone seems to understand a zero, so that is the best place to start. Ask: If I have three positives and three negatives, what do I have when I combine them (add)? 0! That is logical.

Think of the white card and the black card as giving you points. A white card gives you points and a black card takes away points. In Figure 3.6 you see two white cards or two points.

Figure 3.6

Now you get two black cards, as illustrated in Figure 3.7, or you have to take away two points.

Figure 3.7

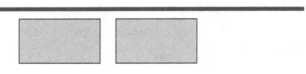

When you combine the two white cards and the two black cards, you have no points. They cancel each other out, and so you have zero. $2 + (-2) = 0$. For each white card, you have a black card; each card cancels the other when you combine them.

Here is another way to think about adding the signed numbers. The number line can be a useful tool to visualize the calculations. Think of the number in two parts: the quantity (spaces on the number line) and the sign (direction). To add positive numbers you move your counter to the right on the number line. For example, $3 + 4 = 7$. Start at 0, move three *spaces* to the right, then move four more *spaces* to the right and you land on 7. The arrows in Figure 3.8 illustrate the movement.

Figure 3.8

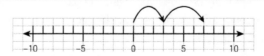

Negative signs may be thought of as indicating moving to the left on the number line. So add $-3 + (-4)$. Starting at 0, move three spaces to the left and then four more spaces to the left and you land on −7. You write: −3 + (−4) = −7. The arrows in Figure 3.9 illustrate the movement.

Figure 3.9

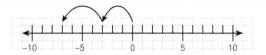

Keep in mind that subtraction may be viewed as the addition of negative numbers. Consider 3 − 4. Now think: 3 − 4 is really 3 + (−4). You can say: I am adding 3 plus the opposite of 4.

Figure 3.10

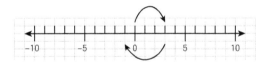

Look at Figure 3.10. Start at 0. Move three spaces to the right. Then move four spaces to the left. You land on −1. A trick to remember: If you see a minus sign indicating the operation of subtraction, change the operation to addition and combine using a negative number.

Now consider −3 − 4. The arrows in Figure 3.11 illustrate the movement. Start at 0; move three spaces to the left. Think −3 − 4 is really −3 + (−4), so move four spaces more to the left and land on −7. Write −3 − 4 = −3 + (−4) = −7.

Figure 3.11

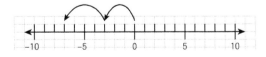

What happens when you are performing the following calculation: −3 − (−4)? WOW! That is a lot of negatives!

So you have three black cards (−3). And you want to take away from them −4 or 4 black cards. How would you do that? You cannot take away −4 because you don't have that many to remove; you only have three black cards to take away as shown in Figure 3.12. How can you find another black card to take away?

Figure 3.12

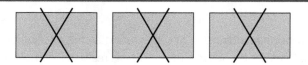

Here's the solution: Add to your collection a zero so you can take away one more negative. Each white and black box you insert is the same as including −1 + 1= 0. Now, as in Figure 3.13, you can take away one more black card.

Figure 3.13

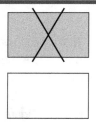

You are left with one white card or +1. Thus −3 − (−4) = +1.

How does that look on a number line? Well, it is helpful to remember that adding (+) always tells you to move in the direction of the signed number whereas subtraction (−) says to turn and go in the opposite direction of the signed number. Here's how to Illustrate −3 − (−4).

Figure 3.14

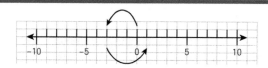

Follow the arrows in Figure 3.14. The expression −3 − (−4) means to start at zero and move three spaces to the left. Then subtract, which means to move in the opposite direction of the signed number. The sign associated with 4 is negative, so move four spaces to the right. Thus, −3 − (−4) = 1. Here is some practice. Can you explain the answers either using a number line or the cards?

YOUR TURN 3.2

Self talk exercise on combining negative numbers

−3 + 4	I am adding so I move in the direction of the signed number which follows the plus sign.	I move three left; then I move four right.
7 − 3	I am subtracting so I move in the direction opposite the signed number which follows the minus sign.	First, I think 7 − 3 = 7 + (−3). I move seven to the right and then I move three to the left.
−5 − (−13)	I am subtracting so I move in the direction opposite the signed number which follows the minus sign.	I move five to the left; then I go opposite to the signed number which follows the minus sign. So I move in a direction which is opposite to the direction indicated by -13, so I move 13 to the right.
8 − (−11)	self talk	Did you arrive at 19?

Multiplication and division with signed numbers also follow rules that make sense based on what multiplication means. Multiplication means finding the total number of items when looking at the contents of a group and the number of groups. For example, you know 2 times 5 = 10. That is just saying that if I have 2 GROUPS and each group contains 5 ITEMS, you have 10 total items. The illustration in Figure 3.15 will help show this principle.

Figure 3.15

Two GROUPS (Think: Row 1 is a group and Row 2 is a group) … each group consists of 5 items … total of 10 items.

On the number line you can easily illustrate two groups of five items. Figure 3.16 displays two arrows, and each arrow encloses five spaces.

Figure 3.16

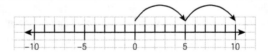

That is the easy part. What happens when there are negative numbers in the problem? Think again about the examples using the black and white cards. What happens if you have two groups with each having five black cards? That would mean you have 10 black cards. So 2 X (−5) = −10. Figure 3.17 illustrates this calculation using a number line.

Figure 3.17

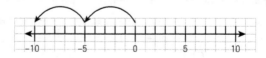

Here is an example: Calculate −2 X −10. First, start with a simple fact: −2 = 2 X (−1) = (−1) X 2. You can think of −2 in two ways. One way is to interpret 2 X (−1) to mean two groups of one black card each = 2 black cards or −2. Another way is to interpret (−1) X 2 as the opposite color of one group of two white cards = 2 black cards or −2. So if you are trying to solve the original problem, replace −2 with 2 X (−1) = (−1) X 2. That helps to eliminate the hard part.

Now substitute that information into the problem you are solving. So, −2 X (−10) = (−1) X 2 X (−10). Do you see how -2 was replaced? Now multiply the easy part: −2 X (−10) = −2 X (−10) = (−1) X 2 X (−10) = (−1) X (−20). What a long equation that is! Do you see how you got the −20? Next, think about what this final expression means: the opposite color of one group of 20 black cards, which is 20 white cards. Congratulations, you got the result: −2 X −10 = 20. Is your brain tired?

You can see how the signs work in a simple chart so you do not need to carry out these thought processes every time you do a problem. If you memorize the chart, then you can multiply the numbers and simply insert the sign based on the chart below. Think of it as the Rule of Signs.

Figure 3.18

Multiply	P	N
P (ositive)	P	N
N (egative)	N	P

Remember the chart is a way to figure out the sign of the answer when multiplying two signed numbers. The sign of the first number is found in the leftmost column. The sign of the second number is found across the top row. For example, multiply (−2) X 3. The sign of the first number (−2) is negative, so look at the leftmost column for negative. The sign of the second number (3) is positive, so look across the top row for positive. Then move your eye across the row next to the negative and down the column below the positive. These intersect at "negative." This means that when you multiply −2 X 3 the answer will be negative.

VOICES FROM CAMPUS 3.1

Lucas

Lucas always had trouble remembering the signs when multiplying. He racked his brain about how to recall the rules until one day he was watching his neighbor's moving van. He was very sad because he felt that all his good friends were moving away. But this led him to a method of recalling the rules for multiplying signed numbers. He felt that "moving away" designated something negative. So every time he says "moves away," he thinks of it as a negative number. But his rule turns out to be something quite positive for remembering the rule of signs when you are multiplying.

When a positive person moves away, that's a negative ($+$ times $- = -$).

When a negative person moves away, that's a positive ($-$ times $- = +$).

Division of signed numbers follows the same Rule of Signs as for multiplication. Multiplication and division are related operations. Division can be thought of as multiplying by a fraction. That means that the sign of the answer to a division question can be found using the Rule of Signs for multiplication. The next section of this book will help you understand the multiplication of fractions.

Credits

- Fig. 3.1a: Source: https://openclipart.org/detail/166637/boy-thinking.
- Fig. 3.1b: Source: https://openclipart.org/detail/86767/tshirt-blue.
- Fig. 3.2: Source: https://openclipart.org/detail/262836/prismatic-man-head-puzzle.
- Fig. 3.15: Source: https://openclipart.org/detail/229335/simple-yellow-smiley.

FRACTION FRACTURE

SOMETIMES IT'S NOT ONLY DENOMINATORS THAT ARE COMMON

4.1: Why Do I Need to Know about Fractions?

Okay, so the idea that 10 is greater than 8 served you very well when you found $10 in your pants pocket, and the pizza that you just ordered cost $8. In fact, as long as your life revolved around whole numbers, things were pretty sweet! Unfortunately, all of those nice whole number relationships that you grew so comfortable with, like 10 is greater than 8, don't always serve you so well when fractions are considered.

 If it's any consolation, you have lots of company when it comes to being puzzled by fractions. In fact, NAEP test results (a test designed to measure US students' understanding of mathematics) have consistently shown that students have a weak understanding of fractions and concepts related to fractions. Recent NAEP test results have revealed that only 21 percent of fourth-grade students could explain whether $\frac{1}{5}$ was larger or smaller than $\frac{1}{4}$.

To illustrate that it's not just elementary students who find frustration in fractions, only 41 percent of eighth-grade students were able to put three given fractions in order from least to greatest.

All right, so how important are fractions anyway? Do you really need to improve your skills in this area? After all, you've made it through high school and are now ready to embark on your next challenge, a successful college experience. And then, with some good luck, you'll find a fulfilling job that provides you with a comfortable living. No need to revisit those past frustrations with fractions, right? Really, fractions are for grade school kids! Actually, you probably do need to improve your ability to work with fractions, since fractions play a key role in understanding proportional reasoning, and the ability to work with fractions aids you in solving problems that deal with percentages and decimals. And it's fair to point out that the ability to work with fractions will make you a better student in any required math classes that you might encounter at the college level.

VOICES FROM CAMPUS 4.1

Aaron
Frustrated with Fractions

Okay, I get that fractions are supposed to be easy; after all, we met them in elementary school. But frankly, they don't seem so easy to me. Sure, when we had the chance to shade parts of a figure to represent $\frac{1}{2}$ or $\frac{1}{4}$, things were going well.

Then it seemed like there were so many ways to consider what a fraction means. Is it part of a whole or comparing one type of thing to another? And don't get me started with having to locate cryptic fractions like $\frac{3}{7}$ on a number line!

Honestly, after a while, I just gave up. I think I could have mastered fractions, but I definitely feel that I didn't have nearly enough time with hands-on materials before we switched off to the rules for fraction arithmetic.

I understand that lots of things in the world involve fractions. I really do. But I must be honest here, I just don't feel very confident when I have to work with fractions. I never knew why dividing by a fraction was the same as multiplying by a reciprocal. To this day, no one ever explained that one to me. I'm still not sure when I need to find a common denominator, much less how to find the least common denominator. Really, does it have to be least? Why?

Now that I've taken some higher-level science classes and seen the beauty of decimals, I guess I just wish that fractions could all just be changed to decimals. Why don't we agree to do that?

4.2: Developing a Fraction Sense

Many people, like Aaron, struggle with fractions and fractional concepts because frequently when they are first introduced the emphasis is placed on computation with fractions rather than the meaning of fractions. Luckily there is a wide variety of models that can help you understand the meaning of fractions, and that should make the transition to computation with fractions less troublesome. Most authors who have considered the notion of fraction sense agree that it's important to realize that fractions can be represented by using the **PART-WHOLE** model. With the use of this model, fractions refer to equal parts of a whole.

Yes, of course you can see an example! Honestly, that's probably one of the reasons that you're experiencing fraction frustration—you just need some more work with the basic models that can represent fractions. For the purposes of this book, the use of multiple models to represent fractions is a good thing. This chapter will consider three different models that should increase your understanding of the basic notion of a fraction: the area model, the length model, and the set model.

Area Model

Think about how you might make sense of the fraction $\frac{3}{4}$. You might make use of an area model—the shapes most often used tend to be a circle or a rectangle. In this case, you divide the geometric shape into the number of pieces indicated by the bottom number in the fraction (the *DENOMINATOR*) and subsequently shade the number of pieces indicated by the top number in the fraction (the *NUMERATOR*). Figure 4.1 illustrates the use of a circle as an area model for $\frac{3}{4}$.

Figure 4.1

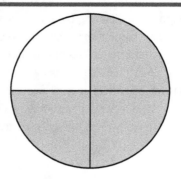

Area models can also be used to illustrate equivalent fractions. You might still be upset about the points that you lost in math class because you didn't "reduce" your answer. Hey, at least you had an answer, right! Figure 4.2 illustrates the use of area models to show the equivalence of the fractions $\frac{1}{2}$, $\frac{2}{4}$, and $\frac{4}{8}$. By using an area model, it's apparent that the values of the three fractions all result in the same part of the rectangle being shaded. Of course, your math teacher wasn't wrong when he tried to tell you that these fractions were equivalent. Unfortunately, many students were just like you—they got bogged down on the processes used to "reduce" fractions and never fully focused on the notion that equivalent fractions represent the same part of the whole.

Figure 4.2

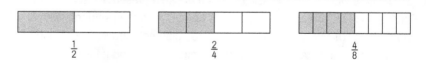

$$\frac{1}{2} \qquad \frac{2}{4} \qquad \frac{4}{8}$$

Length Model

When using length models, we compare lengths or measurements instead of areas. One place where this model has significant value is the consideration of the number line. In fact, lots of people struggle with the notion that a fraction is a number and not a number over another number.

Locating fractions on a number line helps to reinforce the notion that each fraction has a value. In fact, by locating two different fractions on the same number line, we might easily determine which fraction is larger or smaller. Figure 4.3 illustrates the use of a number line to represent the location of a fraction. In addition, the number line model works well to illustrate fractions that have a value that is greater than 1. The notion that fractions can have a value that is greater than 1 can be a bit confusing too.

Figure 4.3

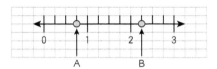

Take a look at the points located on Figure 4.3. Once you realize that the distance from 0 to 1 is divided into four equal pieces, this model makes it easy to represent fourths. Point A represents the fraction $\frac{3}{4}$, and point B represents the fraction $2\frac{1}{4}$. Of course, if you wanted to demonstrate a fraction other than fourths, you'd simply divide the distance from 0 to 1 into a different number of equal segments. A side benefit of this model is that it provides additional practice in measuring lengths. Yes, believe it or not, that carpenter who's working so hard to remodel your house has to be able to easily determine where $6\frac{5}{8}$ inches is located. Oh goodness gracious, fractions are used in real-life applications! And here you thought that your math teacher was just making stuff up.

Another nice feature that can be easily understood by looking at the number line modeled in Figure 4.3 is that between any two fractions, we can always find another fraction. Although at this point in your study of math, you probably aren't too concerned with the density of the real numbers. That idea really gets some people's motors running!

Set Model

The set model is another way in which you can use a visual method to help you to understand fractions. When making use of this model, it's important to understand that the WHOLE is understood to be a set of objects. Then you use subsets of this whole to show fractional parts.

Granted, that sounds a bit confusing. Now take a look at how it might work. Figure 4.4 shows a group of 12 dinosaurs. Sometimes it's easier to designate just what the whole is if you put a border around it. Okay, so this group, or whole, consists of 12 dinosaurs, but there are obviously 2 kinds of dinosaurs shown. Some appear to be stegosauruses (Is that the plural of stegosaurus?) and others appear to be cute blue T. Rexes. If you seek to determine what fraction of the whole is composed by cute blue T. Rexes, you can visualize that you would have four subsets of dinosaurs—each subset containing three dinos. Therefore, you can represent the T. Rexes as $\frac{1}{4}$ of the total dinosaur set because one of the four equally sized subsets was made up of T. Rexes. Be careful here. Make sure to focus on the NUMBER of equal subsets involved (4) rather than the number of items that are in each subset (3). So in the case of these dinosaurs, a set of three dinosaurs represents one-fourth of the set, not one-third.

Figure 4.4

Of course, you also could have represented the fractional part of the number of dinosaurs without using partitioned subsets of three dinosaurs in each subset. If you consider each dinosaur as a unique subset, you'd have 12 subsets, 3 of which contain cute blue T. Rexes. Then you'd represent the fractional part composed of cute blue T. Rexes as $\frac{3}{12}$. It's worth noting here that $\frac{3}{12}$ is equivalent to $\frac{1}{4}$. Sometime later on you'll be given the opportunity to revisit equivalent fractions—you remember having to "reduce" fractions, don't you? Fun! Great Fun!!

YOUR TURN 4.1

It's time for your creativity to shine, and for your sense of fractions to come to fruition (check out that cool alliteration!). See if you can represent the fraction $\frac{2}{5}$ by using each of the three models just considered: the area model, the length model, and the set model. Feel free to use your creative side on the set model! Which model was easiest for you to represent? Why? Which model seemed hardest to represent? Why?

4.3: Fractional Parts: Parts Is Parts

Okay, here's the deal—you've been working long and hard to improve your math skills and develop a can-do attitude about math—it's time for a smile break. Don't get this wrong. Surely you're bombarded with the oldsters in your world saying "look how cool things were way back when," but check this out. Go to YouTube and type the phrase PARTS IS PARTS and watch the commercial. For sure, it will make you smile. Smiles are good!

Parts result when the whole is partitioned or divided up into equal pieces. Sometimes these equal pieces are called FAIR SHARES. You might recall having to share your candy bar with your little brother—the challenge was to break it into pieces so that each of you had your fair share. You didn't give your little brother the smaller piece of chocolate, did you? NO, you didn't. You made sure to divide the candy into two equal portions (i.e., two parts or two fair shares).

A word of caution here. Just because one whole is divided into more parts than another whole, don't be hasty in concluding that a fractional part of the first whole is less than a fractional part of the second whole. Fraction size is relative—a fraction by itself doesn't tell us anything about the size of the whole or the size of the parts. Suppose for a second that you really like pizza and that your two friends, Marty and Manny, each offer you a fractional part of the pizza that they've just purchased. Marty offers you $\frac{1}{3}$ of his pizza, and Manny offers you $\frac{1}{2}$ of his pizza.

Your mind must be working! Marty's pie has been divided into three parts, and Manny's pie has been divided into only two parts. So you might be inclined to take Manny's offer of $\frac{1}{2}$, figuring that it's clearly giving you more pizza than Marty's offer of $\frac{1}{3}$ of his pizza. Hold on for a second. Here's some more information you need before you make your decision. Marty bought his pizza at Hugo's Humongous Pizza—home of the pie that's as big as your dining room table. Manny bought one of those tiny pizzas at I Hate Carbs Café. You know that their pizza is so small that you can eat the entire thing in six bites. Since the size of the whole in Marty's case is so much bigger than the size of the whole in Manny's case, you surely get more pizza if you take Marty's offer of $\frac{1}{3}$ of his pizza. So you see, you have to be cautious when you compare sizes of fractions. You can't just assume that the size of the wholes is the same, or that the fractions are taken from the same whole. Got that? Yes, it's true, depending on sizes of the wholes, $\frac{1}{3}$ might just be more than $\frac{1}{2}$. All right, now you must be hungry, so take a break and order a pizza. You deserve a treat!

4.4: Partitioning

When you "partition" a shape, you divide it into equal parts. A word of caution is needed here. These partitions or fractional parts that you're creating MUST be equal in size (have the same area), but they don't have to be the same shape. Take some time working with partitions and trying to determine what fractional part of the whole each one is. Sounds like fun, eh! Take a look at Figure 4.5 below. What fractional part of the whole rectangle is shaded?

Figure 4.5

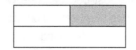

Yes, it's $\frac{1}{4}$, and not $\frac{1}{3}$. Granted, it's a bit sneaky, but you have to consider the sizes of the regions, not just count how many different regions there are. So you need to realize that the big piece on the bottom could be broken up into two pieces, each of which would have the same size as the shaded piece, thus the shaded piece represents $\frac{1}{4}$ of the whole rectangle.

The number of EQUAL parts that the shape is portioned into determines the fractional amount of each piece.

YOUR TURN 4.2

Partitions

Directions: Now it's time to get a bit more creative and take a look at partitions that use different shapes. Each of the shapes in the exercises below represents a whole. See if you can correctly determine what fractional part of the whole is shaded. Don't cheat! The answers will be revealed later on.

Figure 4.6

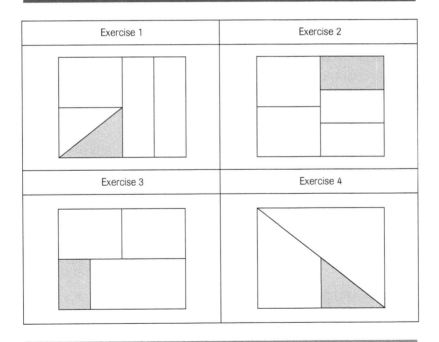

4.5: Modeling "Real World" Problems with Fractions

Now that you've spent some time looking at how you might use models to help you to represent and understand fractions, it's time to move into solving some problems. No, this isn't your idea of a good time, and you're probably a bit nervous. Relax! You're with friends! And most likely you'll be happy to realize that the models that you considered earlier can play a key role in solving problems. Certainly, you've been exposed to countless rules for fraction arithmetic, and you might not know a reciprocal if it fell out of the sky and hit you in the head, but try to persevere here and continue making progress. You can do it!

Nurse Nancy (I Need a Bandage, Stat!)

It's inventory time, and Nurse Nancy is counting the bandages in the office. She counts 48 bandages and notes that $\frac{5}{12}$ of these bandages feature a cute blue elephant. The kids really dig the blue elephant bandages! The rest are standard bandages, suitable for adults and kids who aren't into blue elephants (seems sad, don't you think?). How many of Nurse Nancy's bandages feature the blue elephants?

Now, in the past, this is one of those fraction operation problems that you might have struggled to solve. You might remember your teacher telling you that "of" means "times." And why, pray tell, is that the case? Sadly, the answer to that question was probably never presented! Okay, even if you accepted this bit of sage wisdom as gospel truth, you were still tasked with performing the calculation $\frac{5}{12}$ x 48. Do you need a common denominator? Should you cancel? Do you have to turn the 48 into a fraction? OUCH!

Just look at how this problem might be solved by use of an area model. Figure 4.7 shows how we might represent the 48 bandages by making use of the 12 boxes.

Figure 4.7

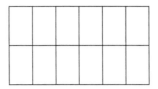

All right, that was fun. Now visualize Nurse Nancy putting bandages into each of the 12 boxes. Remember, she has 48 bandages in total, and some of them feature cute blue elephants. Assuming that she puts the same number of bandages in each box, can you determine how many bandages Nurse Nancy would place in EACH of the 12 boxes? You should be thinking that each box would get four bandages. Good job! Now, recall that $\frac{5}{12}$ of these boxes contain cute elephant bandages. All that means is that you could visualize 5 of the total 12 boxes as those that contain the elephant bandages. That makes it easy to answer the question. If you have 5 boxes that contain elephant bandages, and each of those boxes contains 4 bandages, Nurse Nancy can record 20 blue elephant bandages on the inventory sheet. By use of the set model, it might look something like Figure 4.8.

Figure 4.8

4 bandages	4 bandages	4 bandages	4 bandages	4 bandages	4 bandages
 🐘	 🐘	 🐘	 🐘	 🐘	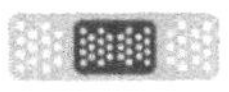 ▦
4 bandages	4 bandages	4 bandages	4 bandages	4 bandages	4 bandages
 ▦	 ▦	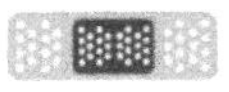 ▦	 ▦	 ▦	 ▦

Beth
Are They Just Making These Rules up as They Go?

I think that one of the reasons I don't like fractions and don't feel very confident when I'm asked to work with them is the emphasis that my teacher made on "covering material" fast. She seemed so concerned about what material was going to be on the standardized test that she didn't or couldn't take the time to let us understand the basics of an idea before moving on to the next thing that involved that idea.

When we started working with fractions, it was actually kind of fun. I enjoyed shading parts of a whole object, and honestly, that made good sense to me. I wasn't ready to move away from that hands-on approach, though. When we started doing arithmetic with fractions, things got ugly. And our teacher wasn't much help, as she wasn't willing to revisit ideas that we didn't seem to understand. Frankly, she seemed to be more concerned with "covering" material than with making sure we understood the concepts. I think that she could have helped me more with my fraction issues, but she seemed too concerned about being on the same page as the teacher next door. Why? What if my class wasn't able to pick ideas up without more hands-on practice?

Well, I'll tell you what happened. To this day, fractions make me uneasy. Sure, I can tell you that $\frac{1}{2}$ is more than $\frac{1}{3}$ (I can always relate it to pizza!). But don't even ask me to divide fractions. The word reciprocal still confuses me! It just seems like fractions have their own weird operations, and I don't really understand them. I can't help but feel that if I'd have had the chance to go a bit slower and build my understanding about fractions, I would be much better off today.

4.6: ABCs of Fractions: Or Maybe the Ups and Downs of Fractions!

The fact is, Beth has lots of company! Many students are totally frustrated learning to divide fractions.

What's a Reciprocal, and Why Should I Care?

Really, why in the world does division change to multiplication? That's beyond weird, right? Hold on tight, maybe it's possible to make some sense out of that seemingly contrived rule that division by a fraction involves multiplying by a reciprocal. Just consider the solution to the problem $2\frac{1}{2} \div \frac{1}{4}$. Come on, you know you thought someone just made that stuff up in an effort to confuse students with more fraction mumbo jumbo! Made no sense then, and maybe it doesn't make any sense now. But see if the modeling approach can help you to understand what is going on. Start by showing what $2\frac{1}{2}$ looks like in rectangles. Each of the larger rectangles represents one whole. So, Figure 4.9 shows how you could represent $2\frac{1}{2}$.

Figure 4.9

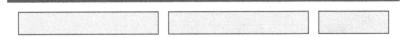

Now, divide what you have into equal shares of four—yes, fourths! In effect, you're getting ready to divide the two and a half (rectangles) by one fourth. Yes, that's the problem: $2\frac{1}{2} \div \frac{1}{4}$.

Figure 4.10

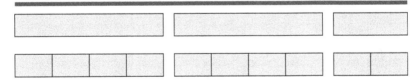

Go ahead, count the small rectangles in Figure 4.10—the fourths. Did you get 10? Yes, you got it. The answer to the problem $2\frac{1}{2} \div \frac{1}{4}$ is 10. In effect, you answered the question, "How many fourths are there in $2\frac{1}{2}$?" You can see that each of the wholes contains 4 fourths, and the half contains 2 fourths, for a total of 10. Great fun! Now in your former studies, you were instructed to multiply $2\frac{1}{2}$ by the reciprocal of $\frac{1}{4}$, which is 4, probably without any clear idea as to why it makes any sense to do such a thing! As the model shows, the essential idea here is to visualize the number of fourths that you would get when you partitioned each of the two wholes and the half into fourths—namely, 10. Makes better sense now that you see the meaning of the 4, doesn't it?

Why Are Common Denominators Needed?

Now turn your attention to addition of fractions. While at least the operation doesn't change, as you saw with division of fractions, the notion of when you need a common denominator and how to find it still can be confusing issues. You can use the modeling approach to look at the problem $\frac{1}{3} + \frac{1}{4}$. Of course, you can use any type of model, but for this example, consider the area model. You can let the entire rectangle represent a whole and picture $\frac{1}{3}$ and $\frac{1}{4}$ as shown in Figure 4.11 below.

Figure 4.11

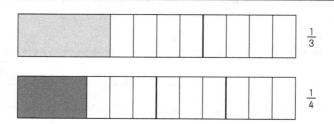

Adding them would simply combine the two shaded portions. Again, you will use the convention that the entire rectangular shape represents a whole. It's relatively easy to see that the two different colored shaded portions would combine to give an area less than a whole (less than 1), but it's quite likely that that's not enough precision. You'll likely have to determine the exact answer to the problem. Figure 4.12 shows the combination of the two shaded portions, giving an area presentation for the solution of the problem $\frac{1}{3} + \frac{1}{4}$.

Figure 4.12

Now, you're savvy enough to realize that the whole rectangle could be broken up into a collection of smaller rectangles. In fact, if you look at the right side of the figure above, you can get a pretty good look at five of these little rectangles. So, if you undertake the challenge of determining how many of these little rectangles it would take to completely fill the two shaded portions, you'd see that the area shaded with light gray $\frac{1}{3}$ would contain four of these smaller rectangles, while the area shaded with dark gray $\frac{1}{4}$ would contain three of these smaller rectangles. Yes, you're right, the big rectangle would consist of 12 of these little rectangles—OMG, you've just found out where the idea of twelfths fits. You see, completely filling the whole would require 12 of these smaller rectangles, so each small rectangle is equivalent to $\frac{1}{12}$.

This convention of using the smaller rectangles $\frac{1}{12}$, has determined that the answer to this problem $\frac{1}{3}+\frac{1}{4}$, as represented by a combination of the shaded portions, is $\frac{7}{12}$. Also, you can see by considering the dark gray area that $\frac{1}{4}=\frac{3}{12}$. Likewise, if you look at the light gray area, you can see that $\frac{1}{3}=\frac{4}{12}$. You've just seen the notion of a common denominator in action. Frankly, you probably wouldn't want to do every addition problem this way, and honestly, it's quite easy to create a common denominator by just multiplying the denominators of the given problem together. However we hope this visual model makes the notion of the common denominator a bit less of a mystery!

4.7: Dividing by a Fraction—Revisited

Earlier, you looked at a problem that asked you to divide by a fraction. You remember the cryptic multiply by a reciprocal rule that was endorsed by your math teacher? Now take a look at what happens when the division doesn't generate a pretty answer. Just for kicks, consider the fair share approach to look at the solution to the problem $3 \sqrt{\frac{2}{3}}$. First look at 3 in the form of three rectangles. In addition, divide each of the three rectangles into three equal pieces (thirds). An illustration of this idea can be seen in Figure 4.13.

Figure 4.13

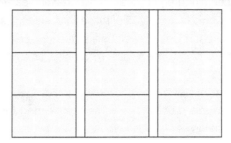

Now for the tricky part—you need to divide this figure into groups of $\frac{2}{3}$. In effect, you are looking to determine how many groups of $\frac{2}{3}$ there are in those three rectangles. See why this solution started by dividing each of the rectangles into thirds? Pretty clever, don't you think! Figure 4.14 shows groups of $\frac{2}{3}$.

Figure 4.14

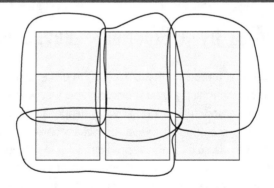

That surely isn't art that will make Van Gogh envious! Each of the squiggly circles represents a group of $\frac{2}{3}$. So, by counting, you can see that there are four such groups, along with a lonesome third in the bottom right side of the picture that isn't included in any of the groupings. Now, here's the tricky part. You must be careful when you represent that leftover piece. Your first instinct might be to identify it as $\frac{1}{3}$, but that's not correct. Remember, you attempted to combine two of the one-third regions into each group. But there is only this one third that isn't part of one of the groups. Hold tight. In the context of this grouping challenge, this one third represents **ONE HALF**

of a group—a whole group would have consisted of two. So, the solution to the problem $3\sqrt{\frac{2}{3}}$ is $4\frac{1}{2}$, because there were four full groups of two and one half of a group. NICE!

Back in the day, you were instructed to solve this problem by: (1) writing the 3 over 1; (2) inverting the $\frac{2}{3}$; and (3) changing the division sign to a multiplication sign. And that's just to start. You haven't even considered how to proceed with the arithmetic to get to an answer. See how the use of the model made things a bit more understandable?

YOUR TURN 4.3

Dividing by a Fraction

Directions: See if you can make use of the modeling approach illustrated above to find the solution to the problem $2\sqrt{\frac{3}{4}}$. Remember to start with two whole shapes that are divided into fourths. Go for it! You can find the answer to this challenge at the end of this chapter. No cheating!

4.8: Multiplying by a Fraction

Next, try to make use of the modeling approach to see what multiplication by a fraction looks like. Consider the problem $12 \times \frac{1}{4}$. If an entire set consists of 12 objects, this problem invites you to consider how many of those objects would be in $\frac{1}{4}$ of that set. Suppose you begin by considering a group of 12 objects, as shown in Figure 4.15.

Figure 4.15

Since this problem involves fourths, start out by dividing the set of 12 objects into 4 equal partitions. Again, tolerate some sub-standard art skill, and check out Figure 4.16.

Figure 4.16

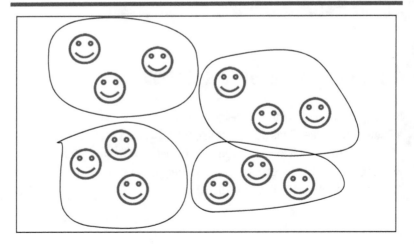

Now, all that's left to do is to determine how many objects are in each of the four equally sized partitions—yes, it's that simple and that obvious! The answer is 3! The use of the model makes it easier to realize that solving the problem $12 \times \frac{1}{4}$ simply requires you to determine the number of objects that would be in each of the 4 partitions of the whole set of 12 objects. Again, it's not that the math is so difficult, or that you'd always want to resort to a model to do every problem, but in all likelihood, one of the reasons that you might have struggled with the solution to this type of problem is the fact that you didn't spend any appreciable amount of time using models to aid you. Instead, you were pushed into the algorithm and got lost! Sadly, you have lots of company.

4.9: Representing a Shaded Region as a Fraction

This is a place where the use of a model helps the process of converting from a mixed number to a fraction to make a lot more sense. You might remember the mind-numbing process that you were instructed to use in order to change from a mixed number to an improper fraction: Multiply the denominator by the whole number part and then add the numerator, all the while keeping the original denominator. Really, who makes this stuff up? Back then, it seemed so contrived and nonsensical. Well, good news, the use of a model makes this process crystal clear. Are you ready? Figure 4.17, shows a model composed of large rectangles divided into four equal parts. You will attempt to represent the shaded area in four different ways.

Figure 4.17

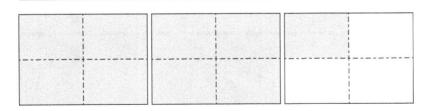

If you agree to represent each large rectangle as one unit, the model above can be used to represent fractions in four different ways. Consider them one at a time. Since each of the large rectangles is divided into four equal regions, you can think of each of these regions as $\frac{1}{4}$. So, you could claim that you have two completely shaded regions and $\frac{1}{4}$ of another region that is shaded—or $2 + \frac{1}{4}$. That would be one way. Of course, you might also realize that this is more conveniently represented as $2\frac{1}{4}$. That would be a second representation. You could get literal and simply count the number of $\frac{1}{4}$ areas that are shaded. In essence that would give you $\frac{1}{4} + \frac{1}{4} + \frac{1}{4} + \frac{1}{4} + \frac{1}{4} + \frac{1}{4} + \frac{1}{4} + \frac{1}{4} + \frac{1}{4}$. This would be the third representation. And, if you simply added these fractions (not hard to do, since they all have the same denominator), you'd get $\frac{9}{4}$. Yep, that's the fourth possible representation containing fractions for the model illustrated in Figure 4.17. Of particular note, focus on the fact that each of the two completely shaded rectangles consists of four "quarters" or a total of eight "quarters." When you combine those eight "quarters" with the lone quarter in the rectangle on the right, you can clearly see that you have nine "quarters". This model makes the process that you were told to use have some meaning—no longer will you be compelled to resort to some cryptic algorithm to convert mixed numbers to improper fractions. Instead you can make use of a model to more fully understand the process and arrive at the answer—with an idea of why the algorithm works. You're welcome!

YOUR TURN 4.4

Representing a Model as a Fraction

Directions: Consider the model in Figure 4.18 and see if you can generate a mixed number and an improper fraction that represent the shaded area. Suppose that a whole consists of seven blocks, stacked on end.

Figure 4.18

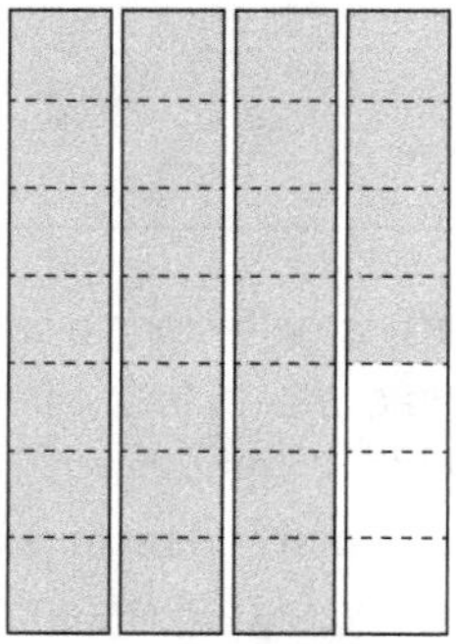

You got it, the correct representations were $3\frac{4}{7}$ and $\frac{25}{7}$. Good work by you!

4.10: Equivalent Fractions

Now, you're going to consider the notion of equivalent fractions. This is actually a pretty significant idea. Unfortunately, it's one that is often misunderstood. You might remember being asked to "reduce" fractions back in the day. Actually, the use of the word never made much sense at all. How do fractions reduce—do they go "no-carb"? The word "simplified" is probably more accurate than "reduced." In any event, you're considering the notion that there are LOTS of fractions that might be used to represent a given shaded area or set of objects in a model. How do you know that the fraction $\frac{2}{6}$ is equivalent to the fraction $\frac{1}{3}$? Take a look at Figure 4.19 to illustrate the process.

Figure 4.19

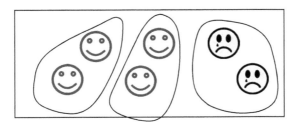

Well, it's obvious that this drawing was done by that same chap with marginal art skills. You can see that the collection of objects consists of smiley faces and frowny faces that are divided up into groups of two. So if you seek to represent the portion of the collection that consists of smiley faces, you could go with $\frac{2}{3}$, since two of the three partitioned groups consist of smiley faces. You could also go with $\frac{4}{6}$, since four of the six objects in the group are smiley faces. The use of a model makes it easy to represent equivalent fractions.

Representing Equivalent Fractions

Directions: Consider the model below and see if you can generate three equivalent fractions that represent the shaded area. Solutions can be found at the end of the chapter. Good luck!

Figure 4.20

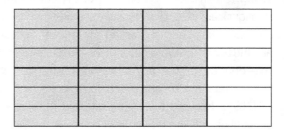

4.11: Comparing Fractions (Benchmarking)

Sometimes what you really need to determine is the relative size of a fraction. Is it close to one; is it about one half; or is its value close to zero? In essence, you aren't so concerned about the actual value of the fraction; rather, you seek a "ballpark" estimate for the fraction. In these situations, you compare the fraction with the "benchmarks" of 0, $\frac{1}{2}$, and 1. Of course, our knowledge about equivalent fractions can help quite a bit here. For instance, you know that $\frac{1}{2}$ is equivalent to $\frac{8}{16}$, so you can surmise that the fraction $\frac{7}{16}$ would be a little less than $\frac{1}{2}$. In a similar fashion, you can conclude that the fraction $\frac{11}{12}$ is close to 1, because 1 could be written equivalently as $\frac{12}{12}$. Knowledge about equivalent fractions, along with the ability to benchmark fractions, provides you with confidence and the tools you need when approximating the value of a given fraction.

Solutions to Selected Your Turn Exercises

Your Turn 4.2 Partitions: Exercise 1 is $\frac{1}{8}$. Exercise 2 is $\frac{1}{6}$. Exercise 3 is $\frac{1}{8}$. Exercise 4 is $\frac{1}{8}$.

Your Turn 4.3 Dividing by a Fraction: $2\frac{2}{3}$.

Your Turn 4.6 Representing Equivalent Fractions: $\frac{3}{4}$ or $\frac{6}{8}$ or $\frac{18}{24}$.

4.12: The Takeaway

- Try to visualize the problem by making use of a model (area, set, or number line).
- Don't rely on "memorized" algorithms. Try to make good sense of what the problem asks you to find.
- Make use of benchmarks and approximations. Is the fraction near one, near one-half, or close to zero?
- Remember, fractions are numbers; they just behave a little differently than "regular numbers." Making use of a model can help. Don't get freaked out because a problem contains fractions.
- There are lots of good sites on the web to help you. Feel free to check out the tool box at the end of this book for a list of valuable resources, including websites.
- Above all else, seek help if you get stuck, get frustrated, or get lost! Talk with your instructor; visit the math center; sign up for a tutor; or maybe work with a group of your classmates. Math is a cumulative subject, and a problem that you have now only tends to get worse as the concepts become more complex.

Credits

- Fig. 4.1: Source: http://www.edupic.net/Images/Fractions/3_4ths_circ_gr.gif.
- Fig. 4.4a: Source: http://clipart-library.com/clipart/6cp5ER9Ei.htm.

- Fig. 4.4b: Source: http://www.kids-dinosaurs.com/images/cartoon-dinosaur-stegosau-rus.png.
- Fig. 4.8a: Source: https://www.wpclipart.com/medical/supplies/bandage/bandage_4.png.html.
- Fig. 4.8b: Source: http://www.clipartlord.com/2016/10/19/free-cartoon-elephant-clip-art-4.
- Fig. 4.15: Source: https://www.pdclipart.org/displayimage.php?album=108&pos=97.
- Fig. 4.16: Source: https://www.pdclipart.org/displayimage.php?album=108&pos=97.
- Fig. 4.19a: Source: https://www.pdclipart.org/displayimage.php?album=108&pos=97.
- Fig. 4.19b: Source: https://pixabay.com/en/smiley-emoticon-sad-face-icon-1635454.

PROBLEM-SOLVING

NO PROBLEM CAN WITHSTAND THE ASSAULT OF SUSTAINED EFFORT

5.1: Puzzling: Poyla's Problem-Solving Model

Jigsaw puzzles are fun, don't you think? Not many people can resist an unfinished puzzle. Try leaving a partially completed puzzle on a table. Soon somebody will stop and try to add a couple of pieces to the puzzle. Puzzles are an activity that can be completed and enjoyed by all regardless of age, ability, or experience. Don't believe it? Just search an Internet store for puzzles and you can refine your search by age group—birth to 24 months, ages 2–4, ages 5–7, ages 8–13, 14 and up, and adults. You can also search by number of pieces. The number of pieces range from less than 24 through more than 3,000!

I'm sure you've probably done lots of puzzles—either on your own or as part of a group. Whether the puzzle took you an hour, a number of days, or a number of weeks to complete, you got a feeling of accomplishment when the puzzle was finished. You met the challenge and you were on your way.

Figure 5.1

Most likely you don't consider solving word problems in math class fun! But word problems are puzzles.

VOICES FROM CAMPUS 5.1

Janet

Dreaded Word Problems

I dread solving word problems. I don't know how to begin solving the problem because the wording of the problem confuses me. I can't "equate" the math numbers, symbols, and equations to the words. Since the problem is a mass of confusing words and I have no idea how to start the problem, I give up.

Janet's words echo the sentiments of many students. However, a jigsaw puzzle–solving strategy can be used as a model for solving the word problems you will encounter in your college math courses. But before you get started on strategy, think about two things: 1) your attitude toward word problems and 2) your expectations about getting an answer to a word problem.

A group of students was asked to describe their attitude toward word problems in one word. The responses were scary, impossible, confusing, frustrating, discouraging, baffling, hard, and difficult. Can you relate to the words in that list?

YOUR TURN 5.1

Rate Your Struggle

Rate Your Struggle with Word Problems

| Piece of Cake | Doable | Hard | Frustrating | Impossible (I give up) |

You're probably wondering … how do I get the nerve, the confidence, the stamina to tackle word problems when I don't even like doing them? Yes, it's hard to begin a word problem—not to mention persevere—when you can't see any way to begin the problem. Most problem-solvers don't worry about correctly starting the problem—it's just about putting the pencil to the paper and beginning with something. If it's wrong, the problem-solver just tries it another way. A problem-solver is patient and does not worry about having to try a couple of ways to get started.

Now, think about the expectations around solving word problems. People who are good at solving word problems seem to get the answer right away. A math teacher can put a problem on the board, do the problem step-by-step, and just like magic the correct answer appears in the last step. Most probably, your personal experience is much different. First, you don't know how to begin the problem and second, even if you do know how to begin it, you get stuck part way through the problem. And then if you do make it through the problem, the answer is wrong. It's completely understandable that you might detest word problems! Guess what? Good problem-solvers experience that exact sequence of issues too! So you're thinking, if that happens to good problem-solvers, why can't I ever get the right answer?

The combination of patience and expectations—as well as a few problem-solving strategies—is the key to being a good problem-solver. Typically, when your teacher or a problem-solver demonstrates the solution to a problem, he or she has worked on the problem for a while and has made many mistakes. However, problem-solvers use mistakes as a way to narrow down the ways to finding the solution. A problem-solver sees mistakes (or missteps) as being informative—just a step that did not work. So the problem-solver continues to narrow down the possible approaches (or steps) that can be used to solve the problem. And most importantly, a misstep does not discourage the problem-solver from continuing to work at the problem. Missteps are part of being a problem-solver! Most likely in math class or when a good problem-solver puts a problem on the board, you are seeing the polished version—nobody wants to demonstrate the missteps!

5.2: Picture It: Step 1

Picture yourself documenting your puzzle-solving strategy while working on a 200-piece jigsaw puzzle. After you read this section, get a jigsaw puzzle of your choice and try this strategy! It will work for a 24-piece puzzle, a 3000-piece puzzle, or a puzzle with any number of pieces in between.

You open the box and dump the pieces on the table. What a mess! It's nothing but a mass of pieces and you wonder how those pieces will ever come together to create the scene on the box! Say to yourself: *When I first read a word problem, I get a knot in my stomach and I wonder how I'm going to determine the answer. But I push that thought out of my mind since I can't worry about the answer. First I need a plan for proceeding.*

You are rooting through the puzzle pieces. You look at each piece to determine if it has a straight edge. If the piece has a straight edge, you set it aside from the mass of pieces into its own pile. When you find the corner pieces (two straight edges), you put those aside in a special pile. I remember being in the puzzle and game section of a book store the other day and seeing puzzle sorting trays to separate puzzle pieces. What a great idea! The trays weren't fancy; you could use any sort of container to segregate pieces, thus keeping the pieces sorted and organized. Tell yourself: *When I begin a word problem, I separate the parts of the problem I understand from the parts I don't understand. Identifying what I know and don't know (just like sorting the pieces of a puzzle) is a step towards finding the solution.*

Now, you have all the straight edge pieces—or most of them. You usually miss a couple when you're doing a large puzzle (a misstep)! But you're not discouraged or worried. You have enough to get started. And you'll find any missing pieces as you proceed. Remind yourself: *I always reread my word problem multiple times because I'll identify information I missed the first time I read it.* Reading the word problem multiple times is critical to making sure you understand the problem you are solving.

5.3: Picture It: Step 2

You may be thinking that you already know to separate the straight edge pieces from the middle pieces. But how do you sort the middle pieces in a meaningful way? Typically, you would 1) sort the pieces by color, 2) try to match and group those pieces against the picture on the box, and 3) place the grouping in the approximate area of the middle of the puzzle frame that matches the picture.

However, depending on the puzzle, that strategy may not be possible. For example, have you seen the puzzles that are pictures of peppermint hard candy? For this puzzle, the puzzle solver cannot sort by color or group pieces by a specific area since most of the area has similar colors and items.

So now what do you do? You cannot sort by color since most of the pieces are the same color. It is also difficult to determine unique areas. In this case, you can sort the pieces by shape. In Figure 5.2, you can see how to sort the pieces by the number of knobs on each piece: zero knobs, one knob, two knobs, three knobs, and four knobs (not depicted in this picture, but a four-knob piece is included in most puzzles). A helpful sub-sort is the position of the knobs. For example, with two knobs, the knobs can be on opposite sides from each other (row 1, column 5 in the picture below) or neighbors of each other (row 2, column 1 in the picture below).

Figure 5.2

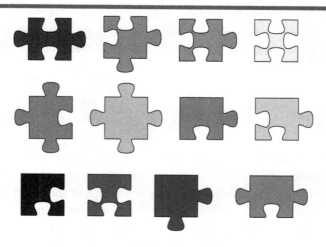

So you are probably wondering how this sorting helps. Try distinguishing the shape (number of knobs) that makes sense for the missing piece. As you add pieces, you can continue searching for possible pieces that match the missing shape. This can be explained with a specific example.

Figure 5.3 highlights the problem. The entire bottom outside frame of this puzzle is grass. Agh! You have all the edge pieces, but you cannot distinguish any of the pieces by color!

Figure 5.3

So you have to depend on the puzzle shapes. You begin to sort the pieces by the knobs. This is not a whole lot of fun, but you know that the time you invest in sorting will make it easier to put the bottom edge together. Do you see seven unique categories in Figure 5.4?

Figure 5.4

Column 1 has two knobs, one on each side; column 2 has one knob on the right side; column 3 has no knobs; column 4 has one knob on the left side; column 5 has two knobs that are adjacent located on the left side and the top; column 6 has two adjacent knobs located on the right side and the top; and finally column 7 has three knobs, one on each side and one on the top.

As you look at the problem, you notice that one of the pieces in columns 1, 4, 5, 6, and 7 could be the next piece since you need a knob on the left side. So you have to begin trying the pieces. Finally you find the piece in column 7 after many unsuccessful tries. But you got it and that's all that matters!!! Figure 5.5 illustrates your success. Nobody is going to ask you how many tries it took to locate the piece! It was very helpful to minimize the number of pieces you had to try. Your approach made the problem a bit smaller and manageable!

Figure 5.5

The next piece can only come from columns 2, 3, and 6. There it was in column 2 after you tried only a few pieces as shown in Figure 5.6.

Figure 5.6

You get the idea now! Remember combining color and shape is a powerful strategy!

So now you probably understand what putting together a jigsaw puzzle has to do with solving word problems in your math course, yes? Take a step back and review what you did, why you did it, and how this can help you develop a process to make solving word problems a bit easier.

5.4: Putting the Pieces Together: Step 3

First, think of problem-solving being as much an art as it is a science. You learned to solve problems by working with experienced problem-solvers: your teachers and experienced colleagues. Problem-solving skills develop over time with practice. You need to be patient, diligent, and resilient. Recall one thing from reading this section: **Problem-solvers do not solve a problem on the first attempt.** So don't get discouraged if you don't get the answer after a single attempt. You may not realize this, but few experienced problem-solvers get the solution on the first try.

Okay, when you began putting the puzzle together you dumped the pieces on the table and started an initial sort—separating the edge pieces from the center pieces. This step allowed you to gain an understanding of the puzzle's complexity and develop a problem-solving approach. In general, all puzzles are similar, but each puzzle also has some unique attributes. Since there are fewer edge pieces than center pieces, your initial task of putting something of the puzzle together—making some progress—is achieved quickly and you felt good about it! Put one in the victory column for yourself! Also, when viewing the remaining pieces, you begin to understand the size (based on the size of the frame and the number of pieces remaining) and difficulty of the puzzle (based on the picture). It also allows you to develop a plan for putting the remainder of the puzzle together.

This approach is analogous to gaining an initial understanding of a word problem. Read the word problem a few times. Take your time and relax. Make sure you understand what the problem is asking you to solve. Write down the facts you know as well as any things you don't understand. Be sure to ask your tutor or teacher about the things you don't understand. This is a critical step! You cannot solve what you do not understand! By the way, teachers do not expect you to understand everything. If you understand everything right off, then you have mastered the material and there is no need for you to be enrolled in the course!

Recall that you had to look at the picture on the box of the puzzle. This is analogous to trying to visualize the word problem you're attempting to solve. If possible, draw a picture depicting the scene in the word problem. Label the picture with information provided in the problem and put question marks on things in the picture that are unknown. Don't try to solve the problem in this step. Just try to gain a visual understanding of the problem. Reread the word problem while looking at your picture. See if the picture matches the problem's description and make any changes or corrections as necessary.

Next, based on your understanding of the problem at this point, see if you can rewrite the problem in your own words or state the problem to another person. If you can't explain it, you don't fully understand the problem. Why should you do this? Often students and even expert problem-solvers solve the incorrect problem. Why? Because they misunderstood the problem. It is worth the extra time to ensure that you understand the problem!

The next tip involves finding a similar problem. Actually there are not that many truly unique problems! So take a few minutes to recall a similar problem or try to find a solution to a similar problem. You can use that knowledge and apply it to the current problem.

Now you are ready to "push the pencil." In other words, try something, anything. You will never solve the problem if you don't make an attempt. Think about putting pieces in a puzzle. It's normal to pick up a piece that does not fit. So what? Try another piece! Eventually the correct piece will be placed in the puzzle. Trial and error is a good approach. Everyone learns from errors. And that's how you will move from a struggling problem-solver to an expert problem-solver.

5.5: The Takeaway

That was a lot of stuff to apply to beginning a word problem. So here's a summary:

1. Read the problem.
2. Reread the problem.
3. Visualize the problem (draw it).
4. Reread the problem while looking at your drawing. Make any necessary additions, changes, or corrections.
5. Rewrite (or re-state) the problem in your own words.
6. "Push the pencil"—apply the mathematics you have learned or are attempting to learn to the problem.

This approach could help Janet get over her fear of word problems and it can help you too! Remember, problem-solving is as much an art as it is a science, so try this approach. In trying it you may find other ways of getting started!

One last word on word problems! Use your understanding of numbers, estimation, fractions, and the problem-solving process to solve the following word problem. You can do it! You learned a lot over the pages in this book!

YOUR TURN 5.2

A Practice Word Problem

How many $\frac{3}{4}$ ounce spoonfuls of flour are in a $7\frac{1}{2}$ ounce bag of flour? Begin by drawing a picture and then try to estimate your answer. [HINT: Consider 1 ounce spoonfuls with an 8 ounce bag of flour.] Then use your knowledge of fractions and arithmetic operations to solve the problem.

Credits

THE TOOL BOX

ongratulations! You persevered and made it through this entire book. Hopefully, you've started to realize that the ability to understand math and to do well on homework, quizzes, and tests truly lies within you. Like many things in life, math ability improves with consistent and dedicated practice. Your newfound confidence and positive mindset will aid you as you enter the math classroom. And, as an added benefit, your enhanced confidence and growth mindset will surely help you in other aspects of your life, as well.

The purpose of this chapter, The Tool Box, is to share information in the form of tips, websites, and articles that you can consult when you need additional help or maybe a more intensive review lesson. Yes, my friend, the information age brings math information right into the comfort of your home! You no longer have to lace up your sneakers and head out to the local library, where you have to rummage through stacks of periodicals and journals to find an article that might help you.

Figure 6.1

Sometimes, the key to success is just having the right tool

Relax, grab some popcorn and a cold soda, and check out the following references for additional help in your quest to better understand mathematics. Each of the sections below will begin with an "old-school" set of tips and strategies that you can peruse when the battery in your laptop or tablet is charging. Then you'll find a chart that presents selected web-based resources (websites and/or sources of articles) that contain a wealth of additional information. Enjoy the Toolbox!

6.1: Anxious about Math?

First, let's recap a few strategies that can help you combat math anxiety. Remember, math is a cumulative subject and your efforts today play a key role in your successes tomorrow. Don't get down; get determined!

Figure 6.2

- Ask questions in class, often; preferably, as soon as you begin to become lost or confused.
- Find someone to study math with. Math is often easier to understand when someone who speaks "your language" helps you.
- Be as well prepared for each class as possible. Review your notes, making sure to study the examples that were done in class.
- Do math EACH day. Even if you have no graded assignment, re-do some problems, or work on some additional problems.
- Don't measure your math abilities against your classmates! Learning math is NOT a competition!
- Try to become an active learner, not a passive learner. Take control of your education as much as possible. The more you feel empowered, the less you will be intimidated when you encounter the challenge of a new concept.

As previously mentioned, the Internet can easily deliver a wealth of information to your browser. Sure, that comes in handy when checking the stats for your fantasy football team, but it's also useful for things like learning. Who'd have thought?! Here are some useful web-based sites that provide information about math anxiety.

Figure 6.3

WEB SOURCE: http://www.math.com/students/advice/anxiety.html	CREATOR/Authorship: Math.com
SUMMARY: The author presents honest talk about math anxiety, and presents strategies to aid students in overcoming math anxiety, and going on to be successful in math.	
WEB SOURCE: https://www.thinkthroughmath.com/math-anxiety/	CREATOR/Authorship: Trevor Alred
SUMMARY: This article presents math anxiety as something that can be overcome, through the development of a growth mindset. The author also considers the role that teachers can play in developing a positive attitude toward math, and the life-long effects of a good attitude about math.	
WEB SOURCE: https://ferris.edu/HTMLS/colleges/university/ASC/reduce-math-anxiety.htm	CREATOR/Authorship: Ferris State University Academic Support Center
SUMMARY: Ten ways to reduce math anxiety. You can do it!	
WEB SOURCE: http://home.capecod.net/~tpanitz/ccchtml/responsibilities.html	CREATOR/Authorship: Kathy Acker
SUMMARY: The math anxiety code of responsibilities. Check out items 3, 6, and 13. You control your own learning, and you control your own emotions related to learning!	

6.2: Number Sense Support

Many of the resources on the web deal with developing number sense at the primary grade levels. Most likely, you're beyond that, and you're seeking help when you are asked to perform operations that involve positive integers and negative integers. Luckily, there are many web-based sites and applications that can aid you in this task. Don't fret. Log on, grab a mouse, and work to improve your skills. The bad news is that positive and negative number skills can always be a source of frustration and lost points on tests; however, the good news is that you CAN improve those skills and, subsequently, lose fewer points on your tests! Here are some sources of support for the development of number sense.

Figure 6.4

WEB SOURCE: https://betterexplained.com/articles/ subtracting-negative-numbers/	CREATOR/Authorship: Kalid Azad @ Better Explained Website
SUMMARY: A witty explanation dealing with negative numbers, and their uses. This website contains a wealth of information, aiding your efforts to understand and learn, and NOT to memorize!	
WEB SOURCE: http://www.math-shortcut-tricks.com/	CREATOR/Authorship: "R" and "B" @ math-shortcut-tricks website
SUMMARY: A very well done set on addition and subtraction—with a variety of number types. Good shortcuts for addition and subtraction.	
WEB SOURCE: https://www.youcubed.org/resource/ number-sense/	CREATOR/Authorship: Stanford Graduate School of Education
SUMMARY: This site provides a link to a comprehensive set of activities that promote number sense, along with the educational aspects devoted to the importance of the development of number sense. You can spend hours here!	
WEB SOURCE: http://www.themathpage.com/alg/ signed-numbers.htm	CREATOR/Authorship: Lawrence Spector
SUMMARY: Having issues with positives and negatives? This site is for you! A great number of examples and practice problems to enhance your skills and confidence in arithmetic involving signed numbers.	

6.3: Fraction Fortifications

If fractions cause you stress, you have lots of company! For whatever reason, fractions tend to cause apprehension in lots of students. But you don't have to feel flustered by fraction failure! Check out that alliteration! These pointers can help you to work through your fraction fractures.

Figure 6.5

- Don't rely on "memorized" algorithms—try to make good logical sense of what the problem asks you to find.
- Make use of a model to help you visualize the problem. Sometimes, one model might be easier to use than another.
- Use benchmarks and approximations—is the fraction near 1, near one-half, or close to zero. Many times, an approximation will aid you, and you might not need an exact answer.
- Don't get freaked out because a problem contains a fraction. Fractions are numbers too. Try to solve a similar problem that doesn't contain a fraction, and generalize your solution.

Again, the web provides a wealth of resources that can aid you in developing your ability to work with fractions. Here are a few resources to get you started. Soon you'll be hoping that a problem contains fractions! Okay, maybe that was a reach!

Figure 6.6

WEB SOURCE: http://ricksmath.com/fractions/	CREATOR/Authorship: ricksmath
SUMMARY: This site has it all: an overview of fractions, along with a good supply of problems dealing with operations involving fractions. If fraction arithmetic is a source of concern for you, spend some time here!	
WEB SOURCE: https://www.youtube.com/watch?v=-6AhN38OR14	CREATOR/Authorship: appuseries
SUMMARY: You knew it had to happen! Here's a YouTube video that details all facets of fraction arithmetic. It's well done, although you'll be here for a bit, as it's also pretty long.	
WEB SOURCE: https://www.mathsisfun.com/fractions-menu.html	CREATOR/Authorship: MathisFun
SUMMARY: Again, a wide variety of activities designed to promote the development of fraction understanding. If your past is littered with fraction frustrations, this is a good place to start to understand fractions in a better way.	
WEB SOURCE: http://www.moomoomath.com/fractions-tips-and-tricks.html	CREATOR/Authorship: MooMooMath
SUMMARY: A series of "tricks" designed to enable you to perform arithmetic with fractions in a quicker fashion. Sometimes, a tip is all you need!	

6.4: Problem-Solving Strategies

Reading a word problem is very different than reading a Stephen King novel. Most times, you'll read segments of the problem as you effectively formulate a strategy to solve the problem. Consider the following pointers that might enhance your abilities to solve word problems.

Figure 6.7

- Read the problem carefully. Make sure that you know what you're being asked to find, and what information is provided to help you.
- Re-read the problem. Actually, you'll probably read bits and pieces of the problem multiple times, as you analyze the given information.
- Draw a Diagram. If appropriate, draw a diagram and label what you know and what you need to find. Sometimes, diagrams might suggest a good solution technique.
- Decide if you can make use of a formula. Try to formulate a plan of solution.
- Once you find a solution, make sure that it answers the question that you have been asked, and determine if it makes sense.
- Lastly, identify characteristics that make this problem like/unlike other problems that you might be asked to solve. Often times, problems have a sort of "commonality". Identifying common traits can make solving subsequent problems a bit easier.

Let's check the web for problem-solving sites, shall we?

Figure 6.8

WEB SOURCE: http://platonicrealms.com/encyclopedia/solving-story-problems	CREATOR/Authorship: platonicrealms
SUMMARY: A great article dealing with development of problem solving skills. Well worth your time to read and study!	
WEB SOURCE: http://tutorial.math.lamar.edu/Extras/StudyMath/ProblemSolving.aspx	CREATOR/Authorship: Paul Dawkins
SUMMARY: A nice, concise, bullet-point list of ways to enhance your abilities to solve word problems. It's worth noting that the author provides a wealth of other math materials on his site.	
WEB SOURCE: http://www.studygs.net/mathproblems.htm	CREATOR/Authorship: Study Guides and Strategies Website
SUMMARY: An excellent portal to problem solving. This page provides a point by point lesson for you to interact with, along with a detailed listing of a variety of math problems, along with strategies for the solution of those problems. Not to be missed!	

6.5: Strategies for Studying Math

Studying for math is not the same as studying for many other subjects. For some students, math seems like a foreign language, and in some sense, studying for math is akin to studying for French or Spanish—you have to know the vocabulary, and to excel in the subject, you need to practice it on a regular basis. Without further ado, here are some pointers for studying mathematics. Enjoy!

Figure 6.9

- Math is Not a spectator sport! To learn and understand the material, you must work on the problems. To learn, you must DO. In that sense, math is a lot like playing music—practice leads to success.
- Math is comprehensive—concepts build on themselves. Make sure to master each concept before moving on. Ask yourself the question: "Do I really UNDERSTAND what I have just learned?"
- College math tends to move very fast, and classes might only meet one or two times per week. Seek help, when concepts don't make sense to you.
- Do math EACH day. But, it's probably not a good subject to "cram". Spending a block of hours at a time probably isn't a good strategy. Instead, carve your study time into reasonable intervals of time.
- Do math at a time of day when you are most capable of learning challenging things. For many students, this means morning is a good time to do math—before your brain gets "tired".
- Create an environment that aids you in your mathematics study. Have your book, notebook, pencils, in a neat locale that affords you the opportunity to concentrate fully on concepts, and minimizes the risk of distractions.

And now, as Spiderman might say, it's off to the web!!

Figure 6.10

WEB SOURCE: http://tutorial.math.lamar.edu/Extras/StudyMath/ HowToStudyMath.aspx	CREATOR/Authorship: Paul Dawkins
SUMMARY: This site features a wealth of good information. You can find pointers for studying math, along with a wide variety of help on specific math topics. Visit—it's almost a guarantee that you'll find something that can help you.	

WEB SOURCE: http://www.makeuseof.com/tag/20-websites-need-learn-math-step-step/	CREATOR/Authorship: Shay Meinecke
SUMMARY: Fight through the advertisements. The author provides a valuable list of sites that can direct you to help in almost any math class.	
WEB SOURCE: https://www.khanacademy.org/	CREATOR/Authorship: Khan Academy
SUMMARY: You name it, they have it! Videos devoted to lots of specific math concepts—from arithmetic, through algebra, and all the way up through calculus. Lots of videos—you'll need that extra-large bag of popcorn.	
WEB SOURCE: https://www.youtube.com/channel/UCT4-UAcRfvBtO76gX-2vexpA	CREATOR/Authorship: YouTube
SUMMARY: Yes, it's a whole channel devoted to learning mathematics! Lots of good tricks and strategies to be found here!	

6.6: Test-Taking Tips

Improved attitudes about your abilities and a lessened fear of math surely will help you to perform better on tests and quizzes. But since tests and quizzes tend to contribute a large part of the final grade in most mathematics classes, it's probably worth examining some pointers that might help you to perform better on those tests and quizzes. No web-based references on this one—just some tried-and-true bullet points for your consideration.

Figure 6.11

- RELAX!!! This is really important, but frankly, it's hard to do. The more you feel stressed out, the more likely it is that you'll "blank out". Don't panic. You can do this!
- Work the test in 3 stages. First, go through the test and do all of the easy problems. Then, go through the test again, and work on the problems that you think that you can do, but aren't sure. Lastly, go over the test a final time, and work on any remaining problems.
- Keep an eye on the clock. Don't spend too much time working on any one problem, or you might not have enough time to finish the entire exam. Sometimes, it's smart to move on!
- Remember, teachers like neat papers! Make it as easy as possible for the instructor to see how much you do know. Try to write a well-reasoned solution. Even if your answer isn't perfect, a well-crafted and neat solution lends itself to a better partial credit score.
- Never leave a problem blank. Even if you don't know how to solve the problem, try something. Any effort is better than no effort. You can't assume partial credit on a solution that you try, but you CAN assume no credit on a problem that you leave blank.
- Make sure that your answer makes sense.
- Recheck Your Work. If time permits go back over the exam and check each problem. If you have enough time, re-do each problem!

Well, as they say on the big Hollywood production sets, that's a wrap! Remember, math is a subject that invites you to succeed. Sure, sometimes the invitation is a bit puzzling, but solid effort combined with a growth mindset will always support quality learning. Go forth and solve!

Credit

- Fig. 6.1: Source: https://openclipart.org/detail/190367/toolbox.

REFERENCES

Akita, L.G. (2014). *Think great: Be great!* USA: Create Space Independent Publishing, LTD.

Bradberry, T. (2015, September 15). *Do you have grit?* Retrieved from https://www. linkedin.com/ pulse/do-you-have-grit-dr-travis-bradberry

Bradberry, T. (2015, September 15). *Why is attitude more important than IQ?* Retrieved from https://www.linkedin.com/pulse/why-attitude-more-important-than-iq-dr-travis-bradberry/

Duckworth, A. (2016). *Grit: The power of passion and perseverance.* New York: Scribner.

Dwek, C. (2006). *Mindset: The new psychology of success.* New York: Ballatine.

Gingrich, N., Bernstein, A. & Bernstein, P. (1995). *Quotations from speaker Newt: The little red, white, and blue book of the Republican revolution.* New York: Workman Publishing Company, Inc.

Hull, J. (2012, September 28). Can basic math skills make you rich? *US News and World Report.* Retrieved from https://money.usnews.com/money/blogs/the-smarter-mutual-fund-investor/2012/09/28/can-basic-math-skills-make-you-rich

Koyenikan, I. (2016). *Wealth for all: Living a life of success at the edge of your ability.* Fuquay-Varina, NC: Grandeur-Touch, LLC.

US Department of Labor. Bureau of Labor Statistics. (2015) Retrieved from https:// www. bls.gov/ nls/nlsfaqs.htm#anch41

Printed in the USA
CPSIA information can be obtained
at www.ICGtesting.com
LVHW010037191023
761494LV00020BA/134